Even though she was only in grade six, Erica Yurken knew she was destined for a glittering career on the stage. Never in any doubt about her own genius, she felt superior to everyone at notorious Barringa East.

That is, until Alison Ashley unexpectedly turned up – beautiful, rich, clever, and as well-behaved as a nativity angel.

Yet Erica knew that Drama Night at the annual school camp would provide the ideal opportunity to get the better of Alison Ashley!

CAST:	Minimum 7 (5 female and 2 male) to play 14 roles, but, depending on the numbers available, other characters could be added for crowd scenes.
DURATION:	Two acts of 50–55 minutes each.
AGE SUITABILITY:	10 years and upwards.

Have fun putting on your own classroom production of *Hating Alison Ashley*.

Also by Robin Klein

People Might Hear You
Hating Alison Ashley
Halfway Across the Galaxy and Turn Left
Turn Right for Zyrgon
Games . . .
Laurie Loved Me Best
Came Back to Show You I Could Fly
Tearaways
Against the Odds
All in the Blue Unclouded Weather
Dresses of Red and Gold
Seeing Things
The Sky in Silver Lace
The Listmaker
Barney's Blues
Thing!
Thingnapped!
The Princess Who Hated It

Also by Richard Tulloch

Stories from Our House
Stories from Our Street
Stage Fright!

Hating Alison Ashley

The Play

Robin Klein

Adapted for the stage by
Richard Tulloch

PUFFIN BOOKS

PUFFIN BOOKS

UK | USA | Canada| Ireland | Australia
India | New Zealand | South Africa | China

Penguin Books is part of the Penguin Random House group of companies
whose addresses can be found at global.penguinrandomhouse.com.

Penguin
Random House
Australia

First published by Penguin Australia Pty Ltd, 1988

Typeset in Caledonia Roman and Avant Garde Book and Medium
by Leader Composition, and Post pre-Press Group, Brisbane, Queensland
Printed and bound in Australia by Griffin Press, an accredited ISO AS/NZS 14001
Environmental Management Systems printer.

National Library of Australia Cataloguing-in-Publication data:

Tulloch, Richard
Hating Alison Ashley: the play.
ISBN 978 0 14 032749 6.

      I. Children's plays, Australian. 2. College and school drama.
      I. Klein, Robin. II. Title.

A8323.3

puffin.com.au

Introduction

This play is a stage adaptation of Robin Klein's best-selling novel *Hating Alison Ashley*.

I first read the book in 1986, loved it, and decided it would be great material for a play. Fired with enthusiasm, I checked with Robin Klein to see that the rights were available, recommended the book to theatre directors, put my copy back on the shelf and forgot all about it.

A couple of months later Nici Wood, then director of Sydney's Toe Truck Theatre, told me she had read the book and would like to direct the play if I wrote the script.

I re-read the book, loved it, and decided it would be terrible material for a play. There were too many characters; there was too little action, too much description of little details, not enough dialogue, etc.

I rang Nici and said I couldn't do it.

Nici said the theatre was already booked, the novel was great, what was the matter with me anyway and besides, if I didn't do it, she'd come round and personally strangle me.

So I did it.

And it turned out to be fun.

• • •

Those who know and love the book will spot various differences in the action and some of the characters in the play. I felt that a few changes were necessary for a number of reasons.

The first problem was with the cast size.

There are over fifty characters in the book and the adaptation was commissioned by Toe Truck Theatre for performance by seven professional adult actors. Even with some 'doubling' of roles by the cast, many characters had to be left out.

The roles were finally divided between the cast thus:

Erica Yurken
Alison Ashley
Harley/Barry Hollis
Mum/Diane Harper
Jedda/Miss Lattimore/Margeart Collins
Valjoy/Miss Belmont
Lennie/Oscar/Mr Kennard

Of course a production with a larger cast could avoid even this doubling and may be able to add some characters in the classroom and camp scenes.

Another problem I faced was that some of the events in the book would not 'read' well on stage.

A novel, particularly one written in the first person, as *Hating Alison Ashley* is, allows us to know exactly what our main character, Erica, is seeing, feeling and thinking.

On stage, unless this character speaks directly to the audience (a device which can become boring if over-used) all this information has to come out through action and dialogue.

Furthermore, Robin Klein often tells us much about her characters through descriptions of tiny details – Alison Ashley's perfect fingernails, Erica Yurken's work folder covered with Superman gift-wrapping paper, Miss Belmont's television-ad teeth, and so on.

Although these descriptions may be a useful guide to the designer of a play, I had to find ways of saying things about these characters through stage action.

This meant that I sometimes needed to alter the details

of the story so that there would always be something happening that would be interesting for the audience to watch.

I felt, for instance, that the photography lesson in the book would need to be replaced, to avoid the problem of the audience not being able to see the details of the photographs taken by Erica and Alison. I substituted an art lesson in which large murals are painted.

Other scenes, such as Miss Belmont's lesson about coal and Erica's play, *Barringa East Hospital*, are described only briefly in the novel, but I could see they would be fun to do on stage, so I tried to reconstruct them from the clues Robin Klein gives in the book.

I hope that, despite the liberties I have taken, the adaptation retains the spirit and the humour of Robin Klein's superbly entertaining book and that those who see their favourite characters on stage will find them much as they had imagined them.

Many thanks to Robin Klein for giving me such a wonderful story to start with, and to Nici Wood and the Toe Truck Theatre cast and crew for contributing ideas and dialogue which appear in this finished version of the script. They also staged a terrific first production of the play.

Richard Tulloch, 1987

Original Production

This stage version of Robin Klein's novel *Hating Alison Ashley* was first performed by Toe Truck Theatre on 3 June 1987 in the Everest Theatre in the Seymour Centre, Sydney, with the following cast:

ERICA YURKEN	•	Melanie Salomon
ALISON ASHLEY	•	Saskia Post
HARLEY/BARRY HOLLIS	•	Jay Hackett
MUM/DIANE HARPER	•	Penny Cook
JEDDA/MISS LATTIMORE MARGEART COLLINS	•	Merridy Eastman
VALJOY/MISS BELMONT	•	Peta Rutter
LENNIE/OSCAR MR KENNARD	•	Benjamin Franklin
DIRECTOR	•	Nici Wood
DESIGNER	•	Colin Mitchell
LIGHTING DESIGNER	•	Bruce McKendry
STAGE MANAGERS	•	Mandy Clarke and Simon Bishop

Characters

THE YURKEN FAMILY

ERICA Ten. A tall flower in a field of couch grass. A hypochondriac and a liar, but destined for a brilliant, glittering career on the stage.

MUM Likes Bingo, plastic flowers, Parents Without Partners, junk food, dancing and window ornaments like pixies sitting on velvet mushrooms.

HARLEY Seventeen. Unemployed (unless lying in a hammock reading books on astral projection counts as employment).

VALJOY Fifteen. Likes bikies, metal-welding, nail varnish, rude t-shirts, horror movies. Yells a lot and slams doors.

JEDDA Seven. Likes horses, books about horses, horse racing, pony clubs, stables, dressing up as a horse, oats. Utterly embarrassing.

LENNIE Mum's boyfriend. A truckie with a bald patch, a Hawaiian shirt and a great, clanging bumper-bar voice.

STAFF AT BARRINGA EAST PRIMARY SCHOOL

MISS
BELMONT
Grade six teacher. Ladylike and elegant, but with eyes like a fly, that can see sideways and backwards and into things which haven't happened yet. Also has a fierce voice and hair which sends out sparks.

MISS
LATTIMORE
The art and craft teacher. Likes weird clothes made of macramé and hand-crafted leather sandals. Her boyfriend drives a Landrover covered with conservation stickers.

MR
KENNARD
A new teacher. Creeps around looking pale and stricken.

GRADE SIX STUDENTS

BARRY
HOLLIS
Likes vandalism, violence, petty larceny of craft-room materials and riding in trains without a ticket. His big brother is a member of the Eastside Boys who terrorise Barringa East.

DIANE
HARPER
Likes make-up, mannequin parades, and bossing people round (a characteristic which she has taken over from Wendy Millson, who had to be left out of this play).

OSCAR
A fat boy, always being picked on by Barry Hollis.

MARGEART COLLINS	So dim it took her a whole year to learn how to roll the library date stamp forward.
ALISON ASHLEY	Perfect. Rich, beautiful, clever, well-behaved ... the sort of person everybody hates.

Also heard, but never seen, are ALISON'S MOTHER and BARRY'S MOTHER.

Settings

The novel carefully describes the places where the action takes place – the vandalised school, the camp, the playground and the chaos of Erica's house which contrasts with the sterile design of Alison's Hedge End Road mansion.

I think it would almost certainly be disastrous to try to represent all this with naturalistic sets. Even if the cost of building were not prohibitive, the time taken in changing scenes would slow down the action and interrupt the flow of the story.

Colin Mitchell's beautiful design for the original Toe Truck production featured simple cut-out painted flats of suburban houses for Act One which turned over to reveal bushland flats for Act Two. A small revolving section in the centre of the stage enabled smooth scene changes from one location to the next.

All the outdoor scenes were played on a bare stage, with atmosphere provided by sound effects and music, and even the interiors were simply represented – a lamp, a painting or a coffee table suggesting the rest of the environment.

The way the actors moved on stage also helped to tell the audience where they were; there was lots of coming and going in the playground, the art lesson, Erica's house and the camp, while in Miss Belmont's classroom the students sat rigidly behind a row of desks.

Where necessary the actors did scene changes themselves as part of the action, moving desks and benches to set up the location for the next scene.

If a large cast is available, it would be interesting to see how 'crowd scenes' in the school and at the camp could help to create atmosphere.

Producers may nonetheless find incidents in the play which are difficult to stage without the resources which Toe Truck had in the Seymour Centre. (Barry Hollis swinging Margeart from a rope after the Drama Night is one which springs immediately to mind.)

In such cases I can only suggest that producers use their imagination, do the best they can with the resources available and by all means alter the text if need be.

Performance Rights

ACT ONE

(VALJOY, HARLEY, JEDDA and ERICA lounge around the kitchen while MUM is delivering a lecture. ERICA sits a little apart from the others and is conspicuously silent throughout.)

MUM   And remember, when he arrives I want you all to behave yourselves.

VALJOY   Oh sure, Mum, we'll be real little angels.

MUM   You don't have to be little angels at all. Just be natural, normal children. Harley, take your feet off the table! (HARLEY does so.) And Valjoy, you're not wearing that t-shirt at the dinner table.

(VALJOY stands to reveal that her t-shirt reads 'I can be very, very friendly'.)

VALJOY   What's wrong with it?

MUM   You know very well what's wrong with it. And Jedda, I don't want you making that horrible noise when you chew your food.

JEDDA   This horrible noise?

(JEDDA demonstrates – a chomp and a horse-like whinney.)

3

MUM   Don't make any horrible noise, Jedda. Now
         listen, you are my children and I am asking you,
         I'm begging you, as your mother, on my knees,
         please, please, please, help me make a good
         impression.

VALJOY   I'm going at five-thirty.

MUM   Over my dead body, Valjoy.

VALJOY   But Blonk and Spike are going around to
         Macca's to see his new Suzuki.

MUM   You can go out with that no-hoper bikie gang
         any old time. Tonight I have a special friend
         coming round and I want you all here to meet
         him.

HARLEY   Who is it? Prince Charles?

JEDDA   Is it a new boyfriend, Mum?

MUM   Not a 'boyfriend', Jedda. Just a friend. I've only
         known him a week.

VALJOY   She picked him up at Parents Without Partners.

MUM   What's wrong with that?

VALJOY   You've got a nerve, Mum, going to Parents
         Without Partners. You've already had two hus-
         bands and I don't know how many boyfriends.

MUM   Lennie's different.

VALJOY   That's what you always say.

MUM   He's kind and he's fun and he's very widely

4

travelled. He's been to lots of interesting places.

JEDDA   Dad used to go to lots of interesting places too.

HARLEY   Yeah, he's wanted in Queensland for selling shares in a non-existent tin mine.

MUM   We don't mention Dad in this house!

JEDDA   Why not?

MUM   We just don't, Jedda. Especially not tonight.

VALJOY   Especially not in front of the new boyfriend.

MUM   I told you, Valjoy, he's not . . .

HARLEY   Is your new boyfriend a truckie?

MUM   How do you know that, Harley?

(A heavy truck is heard pulling up.)

HARLEY   Because a semi's just squashed our rubbish bin.

(MUM rushes to the window.)

MUM   It's him! (MUM runs around the house tidying up.) Now remember what I said! Valjoy, take that t-shirt off. (VALJOY starts to peel it off.) Not here! Go and change in your room! (VALJOY exits.) I'm warning you – all of you.

(MUM adjusts her wig, glances at herself in the mirror and pretends to be busy with something else when the doorbell rings.)

LENNIE   (Off) Yoodle-oo-doo? Anyone home?

5

(MUM opens the door. LENNIE enters, clasping a huge
bunch of flowers.)

MUM   Lennie!

LENNIE   Howdedoody! (LENNIE holds out the flowers) Da daa!
For the best little woman in Barringa East!

(MUM screams with laughter.)

MUM   Oooh! Isn't he a card? (MUM takes the flowers.)
Oh Lennie, you shouldn't have! Aren't they
beautiful!

(MUM sniffs them. VALJOY returns.)

VALJOY   They're plastic, Mum.

MUM   Oh . . . I just adore plastic flowers. So conve-
nient! I do hate watering! (MUM puts them in a
vase.) Now, introductions . . .

LENNIE   No, no. See if I remember. (LENNIE looks around at
the waiting kids.) Harley. Seventeen years old.
Left school two years ago but hasn't got a job
yet. What do you tell them down the C.E.S.,
mate? Do you say you're an out of work admiral
or taxidermist or something? (LENNIE and MUM laugh
uproariously. THE KIDS are unimpressed.) Never mind,
mate, just joking. How're you going, anyway?
Great to meet ya! (LENNIE slaps a passive HARLEY on the
back and wrings his hand, before turning on VALJOY.)
Valjoy. Fifteen. The only girl doing metal-
welding at Barringa Tech. Bet you could show
the fellas a few tricks with a blowtorch, eh? (A
forced smile from VALJOY. LENNIE discovers JEDDA.) You're
Jedda, you're seven and you're horse-mad. Your
Mum tells me you picked five winners at

6

Rosehill last Saturday, including the Trifecta.

JEDDA   Want to hear me call a race?

HARLEY
and VALJOY   NO!

MUM   Go on, let her do it.

(JEDDA chants . . .)

JEDDA   And Take Your Pick leads them into the home turn, with Anti-Plaque looking for a split in the middle, Beldale Beauty boxed in on the rails so its still Home and Hosed a neck in front, the rider goes for the whip on Masochistic two hundred out and it's Masochistic pulling away from Home and Hosed by half a length, Anti-Plaque is third and the favourite Any Money trailing the field.

MUM   Isn't she cute?

LENNIE   Fantastic!

(But JEDDA draws a big breath and starts off again.)

JEDDA   And with a hundred left to run it's Any Money coming from the back with a blistering run gathering in Beldale Beauty with Anti-Plaque . . .

MUM   That's enough, dear.

JEDDA   But I haven't finished yet.

LENNIE   And last but not least – um . . . (LENNIE turns to ERICA but has forgotten her name.) Don't tell me, don't tell me . . . the other girl, in the middle, ten

7

	years old ... um ... I give up. What's your name, beautiful?
MUM	You remember, Lennie – Erica.
LENNIE	Erica, of course. The sensitive, artistic one. Going to be a great actress. Who knows, maybe one day you'll make it into *Neighbours*. How would that be, eh? (ERICA looks sour.) So, that's it. How are we all?

(No response from THE KIDS.)

MUM	They just need a bit of time to get to know you, Lennie.
JEDDA	You want to see my room, Lennie?
LENNIE	Sure.

(JEDDA and LENNIE exit together.)

MUM	Well, they seem to have taken a shine to each other straight away. (No answer from THE OTHER KIDS.) Getting on like a house on fire. (HARLEY gets up to leave.) Where are you off to, Harley?
HARLEY	I'm going to have a sleep.
MUM	Oh yes, off you go then. Tired out after spending all afternoon in front of the TV.

(VALJOY rises too.)

VALJOY	I'm going round to Blonk's place.
MUM	Not till after dinner.

8

VALJOY	We'll grab a pizza at Dominico's.
MUM	You'll do no such thing! I told Lennie . . .
VALJOY	Look, I said I'd stay to meet Lennie. I've stayed, I've met him and now I'm going.

(VALJOY storms out.)

MUM	When will you be back?
VALJOY	(Off) Never!

(Pause. MUM comes back to ERICA.)

MUM	You like Lennie, don't you Erk? (ERICA shrugs.) He's such a scream isn't he? (ERICA makes no reply.) Well, let's see what we can rustle up for dinner.
ERICA	There's only junk food in the fridge.
MUM	Lennie likes junk food.
ERICA	He would.
MUM	What's the matter with you, Erk?
ERICA	And stop calling me Erk! I get it all day at school – Erk, or Yuk, or Gherkin. What a name – Erica Yurken! Sounds like someone being sick in a bucket. (ERICA retches it out.) Erica Yur-ken! Why did you give me a name like that anyway? It's so common.
MUM	Oh, pardon me for breathing, madam. Aren't we good enough for you? Perhaps you'd be happier if we lived in a mansion in Hedge End Road.

9

ERICA   Not much chance of that, is there?

MUM   What's that supposed to mean?

ERICA   At least there's a bit of elegance about Hedge End Road. Maybe if you'd stayed married a bit longer we'd have had enough money to move.

MUM   Erk, if my nails weren't wet from this protein-reinforced base coat that cost $7.95 I'd get up and tan you!

ERICA   It would be better than living in Barringa East.

MUM   Don't knock Barringa East, Erk. There's lots of advantages about living here.

ERICA   Name just one.

MUM   Barringa East Primary School for a start.

(They continue talking while behind them the scene is changed to the school set.)

ERICA   Barringa East Primary School!

(School kids start to enter and mill around.)

MUM   Think of all the nice things the government bought for that little school – a photography dark-room, the table-tennis tables, the free annual camp for grade six . . .

(BARRY HOLLIS is trussing MARGEART COLLINS to a chair. OSCAR supports BARRY.)

ERICA   That's just because we're classified as Disadvantaged.

MUM   You don't give it a chance, Erk. There must be some nice kids there you could make friends with.

(ERICA watches the seething mass of humanity with distaste.)

ERICA   There's not, Mum. They're all really dirty and loud and rough and they make all these daggy jokes and play really stupid games, and they wear these really drooby clothes . . .

MUM   They can't all be like that.

ERICA   They are, Mum. I'm a tall flower in a field of

11

couch grass. There's no-one I could make friends with. No-one.

MUM   Well, if you're going to be so choosy . . .

(MUM exits. BARRY and MARGEART are arguing violently.)

BARRY   Yeah?

MARGEART   Yeah.

BARRY   Yeah?

MARGEART   Yeah.

BARRY   What did you call me, Margeart?

(BARRY pushes MARGEART.)

MARGEART   Take your hands off me, Barry Hollis. My father's a policeman if you don't know.

BARRY   Well my brother's in the Eastside Boys, so you better apologise if you don't want your windows broken.

(MISS BELMONT enters.)

MISS BELMONT   When you've quite finished . . .!

(The shoving and shouting stops abruptly. ERICA tries to sneak off.)

MISS BELMONT   Erica Yurken, where do you think you're going?

ERICA   I'm going to the sick bay to get a Panadol, Miss Belmont. I've got a nervous headache.

12

MISS BELMONT	Nonsense, Erica.
ERICA	I got it during art, Miss Belmont. I'm hypersensitive to Clag glue.
MISS BELMONT	Go to your desk, Erica. Forty minutes of geography will have you right as rain in no time flat.
BARRY	Yuk, yuk, yuk!
MISS BELMONT	Barry Hollis?
BARRY	Yes, Miss Belmont?
MISS BELMONT	Go to your place by the time I count one!
BARRY	Yes, Miss Belmont.

(ALL CHILDREN stand behind their desks.)

MISS BELMONT	Good morning grade six.
CLASS	Good morning, Miss Belmont.
MISS BELMONT	Thank you, you may sit. (MISS BELMONT turns her back. BARRY HOLLIS stands to throw a ball of paper.) I said sit, Barry Hollis! (BARRY sits, hurriedly.) We have a new girl in our class today. Her name is Alison Ashley. (MISS BELMONT beckons. ALISON ASHLEY enters – the most beautiful, elegant creature you ever set eyes on.) I'd like you all to say good morning to her too.
CLASS	Good morning Alison Ashley.
MISS BELMONT	Sit next to Erica Yurken, Alison. There's a spare seat there.

13

BARRY	Because no-one else wants to sit next to Yuk.
MISS BELMONT	That will do, Barry Hollis.

(MISS BELMONT gets her books ready. ERICA watches ALISON unpack her books.)

ERICA	(Whispers) I just adore your earrings. (ALISON smiles politely, but won't talk back in case MISS BELMONT hears.) I'd like to have my ears pierced, only I'm allergic to methylated spirits. My sister Valjoy said she'd pierce my ears with a compass point, but I don't want to end up with blood poisoning.
MISS BELMONT	Now, a quick test to see who was listening yesterday.

(MISS BELMONT sees that ERICA is talking.)

ERICA	I have a very nice pair of earrings at home, soaking in a bowl of antiseptic. (ALISON tries to tell her that MISS BELMONT approaching and is standing right behind ERICA.) They're little squirrels holding baskets of nuts.

(ERICA notices MISS BELMONT and sits straight again.)

MISS BELMONT	The rivers of New South Wales. Anybody? Hands up. (ERICA'S hand goes up, enthusiastically.) Yes, Erica?
ERICA	The Darling, the Murrumbidgee, the Lachlan . . . um . . .
MISS BELMONT	Very good, Erica. It's nice to know that someone was paying attention yesterday. The Darling, the Murrumbidgee and the Lachlan . . .

14

(ERICA whispers to ALISON.)

ERICA   I always pay attention. I think you only hurt yourself if you don't. Most of the kids in this class chatter all the time . . .

MISS
BELMONT   Erica!

ERICA   But Miss Belmont's a fantastic teacher . . .

MISS
BELMONT   We're waiting, Erica . . .

ERICA   She can make anybody shut up just by looking at them. She's got this sort of withering gaze that goes right through you . . .

(ERICA realises that MISS BELMONT'S withering gaze is focussed on her and falters to a stop.)

MISS
BELMONT   That's better.

(But when MISS BELMONT turns away, ERICA whispers . . .)

ERICA   See what I mean?

(MISS BELMONT turns back quickly.)

MISS
BELMONT   We were discussing the rivers of New South Wales. Who remembers any others? (THE CLASS think. No-one has any idea. Then ALISON'S hand goes up.) Yes, Alison?

ALISON   The Barwon, the Namoi, the Macquarie, the Castlereagh, the Paroo and the Warrego . . .

MISS
BELMONT   Excellent.

ALISON   And the Murray is on the border of New South

15

Wales and Victoria.

MISS BELMONT	(Surprised) Very good indeed.
ALISON	We did the rivers at my old school.
MISS BELMONT	So I see.

(A stir from THE CLASS, with murmurs of 'Goody-goody-two-shoes' especially from BARRY HOLLIS who bangs his feet.)

MISS BELMONT	Barry Hollis, if you don't stop kicking that desk there is going to be a hole in the window pane exactly your size and shape in the next three seconds! (THE CLASS settles immediately.) Now, coal.

(MISS BELMONT goes to write on the board. ERICA whispers . . .)

ERICA	That Barry Hollis is the toughest kid in our whole school.
MISS BELMONT	When you're quite finished, Erica Yurken!
ERICA	Sorry, Miss Belmont.
MISS BELMONT	I should think so too. You will of course remember from the work we did yesterday that coal is a major item in Australia's economy, and that for homework last night I asked you to write down three common uses of coal, such as . . .

(ERICA's hand shoots up.)

ERICA	Home heating, Miss Belmont.
MISS BELMONT	Home heating is a common use of coal, yes. (ALISON's hand goes up.) Yes, Alison?

16

ALISON   In Europe, lumps of coal are burned in many
                homes in winter, but in Australia coal is more
                commonly used in the form of brown coal
                briquettes.

MISS   Very good, Alison.
BELMONT

ALISON   Coal is also used in Australia to produce
                electricity.

MISS   Indeed it is, Alison. So, coal is used for home
BELMONT   heating. Coal is used in the production of
                electricity. And what else can we use coal for?
                Anybody? (ERICA and ALISON's hands go up.) Let's not
                always see the same hands. (MARGEART's hand goes
                up tentatively.) Yes, Margaret Collins?

MARGEART   Um . . .

                (MARGEART has forgotten what she wanted to say.)

MISS   I beg your pardon?
BELMONT

MARGEART   (Repeats more clearly) Um.

MISS   What were you going to tell us, Margaret?
BELMONT

MARGEART   I forget, Miss Belmont.

                (Groans from THE CLASS. ERICA whispers . . .)

ERICA   That Margeart Collins is the dumbest kid in our
                class. Her real name is Margaret, but she's so
                dumb she always writes 'Margeart' so that's
                what we call her.

MISS   Perhaps you were going to tell us another thing
BELMONT   coal is used for, Margaret.

| MARGEART | Oh yes, salad. |

MISS BELMONT: Salad, Margaret?

MARGEART: We had salad with coal in it last night.

MISS BELMONT: Coal salad?

MARGEART: Mum makes it with cabbage and mayonnaise. It's called coal slaw salad really.

(Reaction from THE CLASS.)

ERICA: She is so dumb!

MISS BELMONT: That will do! At least Margaret took the trouble to think about her homework, which is more than I can say for some others who shall remain nameless. Diane Harper, Barry Hollis . . . (DIANE and BARRY look embarrassed.) Now,there are two main classes of coal, these being . . .

(ERICA'S hand goes up.)

ERICA: Black coal?

MISS BELMONT: Black coal and . . .

(ALISON'S hand goes up.)

ALISON: Brown coal . . .

MISS BELMONT: Very good, Alison.

ALISON: . . . otherwise known as lignite.

MISS BELMONT: Excellent. Now brown coal is used mainly for . . .

18

(ERICA calls . . .)

ERICA   Electricity.

MISS   Correct Erica. (ERICA looks smugly at ALISON.) But
BELMONT next time don't call out please. (ALISON's hand goes
         up.) Yes, Alison?

ALISON   Even though brown coal is a low grade of coal it
         is readily available and can be mined by the
         open-cut method.

MISS   Excellent. Now, the major deposits of brown
BELMONT coal are in . . .

(ERICA's hand goes up.)

ERICA   Victoria, Miss Belmont.

MISS   In Victoria . . .(ALISON's hand goes up.) Yes, Alison?
BELMONT

ALISON   In the Latrobe Valley, chiefly around Yallourn
         and Morwell.

MISS   Yes, and . . .
BELMONT

ALISON   There are also other coal measures at Bacchus
         Marsh and Altona.

MISS   Yes, Alison . . .
BELMONT

ALISON   And there was also black coal mined at
         Wonthaggi, but the mine closed in 1968.

MISS   Did it now?
BELMONT

ALISON   We did coal at my old school.

19

MISS BELMONT	So I see. Now, the major deposits of coal in New South Wales are in . . . (ALISON'S hand goes up. ERICA puts her hand up too, desperately waving it as if in agony.) Come on, the rest of you, let's not always see the same hands.

(The bell rings. BARRY HOLLIS' hand shoots up, as does DIANE'S.)

MISS BELMONT	That's better. Barry?

BARRY	The bell's gone, Miss.

(MISS BELMONT sighs.)

MISS BELMONT	All right, grade six, you may go out. (THE CLASS runs for the door.) Don't push! (They slow down.) Perhaps, Erica, you could show Alison around the school?

(MISS BELMONT exits. ERICA looks at ALISON with suspicion.)

ERICA	Do you want to see our school?

ALISON	Thank you, Erica, I'd like that.

(ERICA and ALISON walk into the playground.)

(ERICA and ALISON walk around in the playground.)

ERICA   There's the toilet block.

ALISON   Oh yes, Miss Belmont showed me that.

ERICA   And that's our library over there. It's architect-designed.

ALISON   Oh. At my old school the library was about three times that size.

(BARRY HOLLIS and OSCAR enter, fighting over a skateboard. MISS LATTIMORE enters.)

MISS LATTIMORE   Barry Hollis! (BARRY crosses to her.) Have you been writing rude messages in the library books?

BARRY   That's for me to know and you to find out.

(MISS LATTIMORE shows him a book.)

MISS LATTIMORE   'Fat and Skinny had a race Skinny's pants were a disgrace . . .' (MISS LATTIMORE is about to read more, but it is too rude, so she shows BARRY. OTHER KIDS crowd round too, giggling.) Go away, it's not at all funny! (They move back. BARRY sidles off.) Not you, Barry Hollis. You wait for me outside the staffroom.

(BARRY exits.)

ERICA   And that's the sandpit for the little kids. Only
         you shouldn't go near the Tonkins. They always
         have nits. Did you know lice can jump?

ALISON   Really?

ERICA   They can jump from one kid's head to another
         kid's head.

(MISS LATTIMORE spots them.)

MISS   Hello, you're the new girl, Alison Ashley, aren't
LATTIMORE you?

ERICA   That's right, Miss Lattimore. I'm showing her
         around the school.

MISS   I hear you have a reading age of 14.6, Alison.
LATTIMORE

ALISON   Oh, I don't know about that. I just like reading.

MISS   You must be a very clever girl.
LATTIMORE

ALISON   My aunt is a librarian.

MISS   Really, Alison? How interesting!
LATTIMORE

(MISS LATTIMORE exits. ERICA, who has been feeling left
out, is jealous.)

ERICA   14.6! Fancy boasting like that about having a
         reading age of 14.6!

ALISON   I wasn't boasting.

ERICA   'I just like reading. My aunt is a librarian!'

22

ALISON	But she is a librarian. At my old school . . .
ERICA	Those are the bubblers over there if you want a drink.
ALISON	Oh, I don't usually drink from those. You can catch germs from kids putting their mouths right down on the spout.
ERICA	And there's the tuckshop. They have beaut iced doughnuts.
ALISON	I'm not allowed to eat junk food. I always bring lunch from home.

(BARRY HOLLIS enters with MISS LATTIMORE in pursuit.)

MISS LATTIMORE	Barry . . . Barry Hollis!

(BARRY runs off.)

ERICA	What did he do, Miss Lattimore?
MISS LATTIMORE	He poured tomato sauce in my box of paper clips. I'll kill him!

(MISS LATTIMORE exits after BARRY.)

ERICA	I can show you the sick bay.
ALISON	Oh, no thanks.
ERICA	Why not?
ALISON	Oh, just . . . I don't like looking at grazed knees or anything like that.
ERICA	I've got the longest report on any medical card

23

in the school office.

ALISON   Oh?

ERICA   It says I'm prone to nervous headaches, rhinitis, sinusitis and bee-sting allergy.

ALISON   Really?

ERICA   And I have suspected hypersensitivity to wattle pollen, horsehair, dust mite, clover and Clag glue.

ALISON   Oh!

ERICA   And I've been tested for diabetes and arthritis and gallstones and I don't have to put my head under water when we go swimming because of a punctured eardrum. (ALISON looks green.) What's the matter, Alison Ashley?

ALISON   I don't like illness.

(ERICA looks at ALISON in horror.)

ERICA   You don't like illness?

ALISON   At my old school . . .

ERICA   Yes, I'm sure your old school was much better than Barringa East! Well, Miss Belmont asked me to show you round and I have. So now I can get back to my FRIENDS!

(ERICA leaves ALISON standing as she storms away from her. OTHER KIDS have left, or leave as soon as she approaches them. For a moment she considers rejoining ALISON, but then turns away. ALISON exits,

24

(wondering how she has offended. ERICA pulls out a play script from her bag and begins to study it.)

ERICA   I'm Pirate Peg, the fiercest maid,
That sails the Spanish Main.
I'll fill my hold with plundered gold
'Ere I return to Spain.

(Behind her the scene changes back to her house as she continues rehearsing.)

(MUM sits at the kitchen table, with VALJOY giving her a manicure.)

MUM   The only reason you go to tech is for the boys. Admit it, Valjoy. You just love being the only girl in a class of twenty randy male crane drivers.

VALJOY   What about you and Lennie?

MUM   What about me and Lennie?

VALJOY   Always pashing on in the kitchen when you think we're not looking.

(ERICA enters and continues her rehearsal . . .)

ERICA   So hoist the skull and crossbones,
And load the cannons grim,
For Captain Blood approaches
And we must prepare for him!

VALJOY   Shut up, Erk!

MUM   It's not what you think, Valjoy. Lennie's very good company. And he does all his own repairs and maintenance on his truck and he's widely travelled. Last year he went to Brisbane seven times.

26

ERICA   Nay, nay, ha, ha, old Captain Blood,
        Such thing will never be.
        Come hearties, make him walk the plank
        And splash into the sea . . .

VALJOY Erk!

ERICA   I have to practise somewhere, don't I?

MUM   What's wrong with your room?

ERICA   Jedda the horse freak's in there. She's trying to
        get her teddy to eat oats from a nosebag.

MUM   Valjoy's room then.

VALJOY No! Last time she pinched all my Charlie
        perfume. And where are my gold pendant
        earrings?

ERICA   I didn't touch them!

VALJOY I don't know why you have to practise lines
        anyway. You're not even in the play.

ERICA   I will be. Every year on Drama Night at the year
        six camp they do *Pirate Peg of the Jolly Roger*.
        I'm going to have all the lines learnt before
        then, so they'll have to have me as the star.

        (LENNIE enters.)

LENNIE Howdeedoody everybody. How's my favourite
        movie star today? (LENNIE picks up ERICA's script.)
        'Pirate Peg of the Jolly Roger'. Looks like pretty
        exciting stuff. Hope you won't be making us all
        walk the plank.

27

MUM	Lennie's taking us all to the drive-in tonight, Erk.
ERICA	In his truck?
MUM	Of course.
ERICA	What if I see someone I know?
MUM	What if you do? Honestly, Erk, you're getting that sour and critical lately. You can't drive round everywhere in a golden Mercedes, you know.
ERICA	Alison Ashley does.
MUM	Who's Alison Ashley?
ERICA	Just a kid at school.
MUM	Can't be many kids from Barringa East with a golden Mercedes.
ERICA	She's not from Barringa East. She lives in Hedge End Road.
VALJOY	Oooh, very flash.
LENNIE	Those Mercedes are piss-weak anyway. A BMW handles much better. Or a Porsche.
MUM	Are you a bit jealous of this Alison Ashley, Erk?
ERICA	Of course not. But at least Alison Ashley wouldn't have to go to the drive-in in Lennie's truck. Alison Ashley wouldn't have to listen to boring Lennie's boring jokes all the time.

28

MUM   I won't have you saying things like that about Lennie, Erica!

ERICA   Well he is boring! He's the most boring bloody person I know.

MUM   And don't use that sort of language in this house!

ERICA   Why not? Lennie does! He sits there swearing his head off all the time and you just think it's ordinary conversation. If you can call what Lennie says conversation!

MUM   That's it! Go to your room! (ERICA storms out of the room.) I'm sorry, Lennie.

        (MUM and LENNIE pack up the kitchen set and exit.)

ERICA   (Dramatically) Life is full of injustice. (ERICA throws herself down in tears.) I wish I were dead! (She likes the sound of this, and rehearses it with different dramatic emphases.) I *wish* I were dead! I wish I *were* dead! I wish I were *dead*! I wish I . . . I wish I were Alison Ashley. I wish I could look like her, and talk like her, and have the same clothes and pretty manners. And I wish she would let me be her best friend. Even though I hate her. Life is full of injustice.

        (Behind her the scene changes back to the school playground.)

(MISS LATTIMORE enters. She carries a box of paint and brushes, a large sheet of plastic and a number of sheets of butcher's paper.)

MISS LATTIMORE Get up, Erica. There's no need to be so melodramatic. (MISS LATTIMORE calls off stage.) Over here, grade six! (ERICA gets up. ALISON, OSCAR, DIANE and BARRY enter.) Today in art and craft we're going to do something a bit different. We're going to do some painting out here in the playground ... Barry Hollis, don't put that in your mouth. It's so unhygienic. (ERICA starts to tear up the paper.) Now I want each of you to take a large piece of paper ... wait till I say ... take a large piece of paper and stick it up somewhere. When we're standing quietly in our places ... (MISS LATTIMORE waits for silence, then continues in a soothing, settling voice.) Right, come and get your paper ... now.

(All hell breaks loose as THE KIDS scrabble for paper. ALISON and ERICA spread the plastic on the ground. THE KIDS hang the butcher's paper around the set.)

DIANE Who's got the masking tape?

OSCAR Get out! That's my spot!

ALISON Can you help me hold mine?

30

DIANE   The wind's too strong, Miss.

OSCAR   Get out, Barry!

DIANE   Who's got the masking tape?

OSCAR   Miss, make him stop that!

MISS   Settle down, the lot of you or we'll go straight
LATTIMORE back inside and finish that dictation about Tom
         Roberts. (THE KIDS settle. By now, everyone has their
         paper up and is starting to work with the paint. OSCAR
         can't get started.) What's the matter, Oscar?

OSCAR   I can't think of anything to do, Miss.

MISS   Well, just look around you. There are all sorts of
LATTIMORE things to paint in the world. The artist's eyes are
         his first tool, you know. Shut up, Barry Hollis.
         (OSCAR looks blank.) Would you like me to do a
         squiggle to get you started?

OSCAR   Yes, Miss.

         (MISS LATTIMORE starts to paint on his paper.)

DIANE   Hey, look what Barry's doing.

         (KIDS crowd round to look. MISS LATTIMORE crosses to
         them. The painting is obscured by a crush of
         bodies. They part to allow MISS LATTIMORE through. The
         work is still obscured from view. She tears up the
         painting.)

MISS   Go away, it's not at all funny. If you can't think of
LATTIMORE anything better to paint Barry Hollis, you can go
         and wait over there till the lesson's over.

31

(BARRY exits.)

DIANE   Miss?

MISS LATTIMORE   Yes, Diane?

DIANE   Do we have to do something outside?

MISS LATTIMORE   What do you mean?

DIANE   Well, is it all right if I just do a dress design for my painting?

MISS LATTIMORE   You know that's not really the idea, Diane.

DIANE   But I've got this really good idea for one, Miss. It sort of falls off the shoulder and it's got all sequins down here and it'd be really easy to draw, Miss.

MISS LATTIMORE   Well, perhaps . . .

DIANE   I could do a netball court in the background.

MISS LATTIMORE   All right, please yourself. (MISS LATTIMORE moves across to where ALISON and ERICA are working.) How are you going, Alison?

(ALISON has made a rather cool collage, using a torn sheet of newspaper glued to the paper as a skyline, highlighted with a blue line representing sky.)

ALISON   It's not much at the moment. Just an idea.

MISS LATTIMORE   It's really wonderful, Alison. It's really excellent work for someone your age. Come on, Erica Yurken, get a wriggle on.

32

(MISS LATTIMORE moves off. ERICA hasn't started yet.)

ALISON   What are you doing, Yuk? You haven't even started.

ERICA   That's because mine is going to be very different and original. Anyone can stick up a few bits of torn newspaper.

(ERICA starts to attack her paper, first smearing and dribbling paint, then splashing and throwing à la Jackson Pollock. MISS LATTIMORE stops her.)

MISS LATTIMORE   Erica Yurken!

ERICA   Yes, Miss Lattimore?

MISS LATTIMORE   I warned everyone about throwing paint.

ERICA   But I have to, Miss. I'm doing a modern abstract.

MISS LATTIMORE   All right. But no splashing! (Calls off) Barry Hollis, get off that rubbish bin and let that person out immediately!

(MISS LATTIMORE exits. THE GIRLS continue working on their paintings.)

ERICA   Are you going to the high school or the tech next year, Alison?

ALISON   Actually, I . . .

ERICA   At Barringa High School they flush your head down the toilet as a welcoming ceremony.

ALISON   Well, I . . .

33

ERICA   My sister Valjoy's at the tech. She's the only female in the metal-welding class.

ALISON   Oh!

ERICA   Which will you be going to?

ALISON   I won't be going to either. My mother put my name down for Kyle Girls' Grammar School.

ERICA   Kyle Girls' Grammar School! With the pale-blue uniforms and little bowler hats and gloves! They don't teach you anything there except how to cook for dinner parties and play tennis.

ALISON   It had the highest HSC results of any school in the State last year.

ERICA   Barringa High's got a new science block and for sport they do scuba-diving, and they have sit-in strikes and mass demonstrations and lots of other interesting things!

ALISON   Well at Kyle you can study ballet!

(ERICA fumes. MISS LATTIMORE returns.)

MISS LATTIMORE   All right, everybody, it's nearly clean-up time. Come over here. (BARRY HOLLIS zooms in, wearing a superman cape made from a sheet of butcher's paper with 'Eastside Boys' scrawled on the back.) I'd just like you all to see what some of our better students can achieve. (KIDS crowd around.) Alison wasn't satisfied with just using the paint and paper I gave her. She found newspaper to add a very original textural dimension to her work. And Erica's been doing something . . . abstract. (Everyone looks at ERICA's work. It is a total mess.) What

34

	is it, Erica, dear?
ERICA	It's um . . .
OSCAR	Leprosy.
BARRY	Skin disease.
DIANE	Acne and blackheads.
OSCAR	A body that's been left in the sea.
DIANE	Skin peeling after sunburn.
MISS LATTIMORE	Be sensible, please.
BARRY	It's got a rude word in it.
DIANE	Where?
BARRY	Look. (He turns the painting upside down. The word 'bum' appears.) It says . . .
MISS LATTIMORE	That's enough, Barry! We all know what it says.
ERICA	I didn't mean . . .

(MISS LATTIMORE tears up the painting. The bell rings.)

MISS LATTIMORE	All right, clean up the mess and back to class.

(They do so. ALISON tries to comfort Erica.)

ALISON	It's a pity about your painting, Yuk. I thought it was very original. It's a shame it has to end up in the bin . . .

(But ERICA turns on ALISON.)

35

ERICA   You think you're better than anyone else at
         Barringa East, Alison Ashley. Well, you've got to
         be careful who you pick on at this school.

ALISON   Who said I was picking on anyone?

ERICA   Let me tell you, Alison Ashley, I have some
         powerful friends at this school who don't like
         me being picked on. In school hours or out of
         school hours. If you go on showing me up all the
         time I'll have no alternative.

ALISON   Than what?

ERICA   Than to get my best friend Barry Hollis to bash
         you up.

         (ALISON sees that BARRY is standing behind her.)

ALISON   Well then, why don't you ask him now, Yuk?

         (But, of course, ERICA can't.)

ERICA   You think you're so great, Alison Ashley!

BARRY   Good on yer, Yuk! Fight, fight, fight . . .

ALISON   You mind your own business, Barry Hollis!

         (BARRY exits. The scene changes back to ERICA's
         house.)

ERICA   Just because you've got rich parents who can
         afford to send you to Kyle Girls' Grammar
         School. Well, I wouldn't want to go there if they
         paid me!

         (ALISON exits.)

(ALISON exits. MUM enters, with LENNIE pursuing her,
trying to get a cuddle. ERICA watches with disgust.)

ERICA   Mum?

MUM   Yes, Erk?

ERICA   Can I go to Kyle Girls' Grammar next year?

MUM   Kyle Girls' Grammar? With the pale-blue
dresses and the little bowler hats and gloves?

ERICA   Yes.

MUM   They don't teach you anything there except
how to cook for dinner parties and play tennis.

ERICA   You can learn ballet dancing.

LENNIE   Belly dancing? That'd be good. Come on Erk,
do us a belly dance.

(LENNIE mimes grotesquely. VALJOY enters.)

VALJOY   Erk, I thought I told you not to wear my slave
bangles to school.

LENNIE   Erk can be my slave girl any old tick of the clock.

37

MUM We're having a barbeque tonight, Erk.

(JEDDA cheers.)

ERICA Can't we ever eat anything except junk food?

VALJOY I won't be here. Spider and Blonk are taking me to the drive-in to see *Claws of Blood*. (The doorbell rings.) I'll get it. That'll be Spider.

(VALJOY exits. LENNIE grabs a squealing MUM and pulls her onto his knee.)

LENNIE Come on, Mum. How about a kiss?

MUM Oooh, Lennie, you're awful!

ERICA Hear, hear.

(VALJOY returns.)

VALJOY Erk, there's a kid from your school wants to see you. Can't think why.

(ALISON enters.)

MUM Hello, love, you in the same class as Erk?

ALISON I took home Erica's pencil case by mistake, Mrs Yurken. I thought I'd better return it because of all the homework we've got to do over the weekend.

MUM Say thank-you for the pencil case, Erk. Where's your manners?

ERICA Thanks. (Pause) Um, Alison, this is my mum, and

38

this is my sister Valjoy and my other sister Jedda
and . . .

(She falters to a stop when she gets to LENNIE, but he
stretches out his hand.)

LENNIE Lennie's the handle. Hey, sweetheart, you're a
good-looker. Reckon I'll go back to school.
Fillies didn't look like you when I was at school.

MUM Tell you what, love. We're having a barbeque,
so why don't you stay and have tea with us?

(ERICA wills ALISON to say 'no'.)

ERICA Say 'no'! Please Alison, say 'NO'!

ALISON Thank you very much for the invitation, Mrs
Yurken.

MUM Sure your mum wouldn't mind?

(ERICA sends another message.)

ERICA Yes, she'd hate it! Say you're not allowed!

ALISON Oh no, she wouldn't mind, as long as I get home
by dark.

(ERICA is in agony.)

MUM Fine! You and Erk might want to play records
until tea's ready.

ERICA No! No!

MUM Erk's just mad about that group Splurge. She
plays their album non-stop.

39

ERICA How embarrassing! (MUM, VALJOY and LENNIE exit.) That's not really true, what Mum said about me liking Splurge. My little sister Jedda's the one who's rapt in Splurge.

JEDDA No, I'm not.

ERICA Yes, you are!

ALISON Was that your dad?

(Pause.)

ERICA Certainly not!

ALISON I thought he must be your dad because your mother was . . . you know.

ERICA He's a friend of hers. But she really doesn't like him. He's not her real boyfriend or anything. Her real boyfriend's fantastic. He's very hand-some and he owns a racehorse stud-farm and a Mercedes.

ALISON Really?

ERICA My real father is dead.

JEDDA I thought he was in Queensland.

ERICA He's dead in Queensland.

ALISON Oh, I'm sorry.

(ERICA pushes JEDDA out of the room.)

ERICA He was killed in a plane crash. He was a test pilot. When he knew his plane was going to

40

crash he flew out over the ocean and crashed there so he wouldn't come down on any houses. Mum never got over it.

ALISON   I thought you said she had a boyfriend with a racehorse stud-farm.

ERICA   What's that got to do with it? My mum's very popular.

(Pause)

ALISON   Um . . . Nice house.

ERICA   We're only living here because my brother is training to be a missionary. Our real house is over near Kyle Grammar. Lennie, the man you saw outside, is a security guard there.

(JEDDA enters).

JEDDA   Erk, the barbeque's ready. (To ALISON) Want to hear me call a race?

ERICA   No, she doesn't.

(But JEDDA launches into it . . .)

JEDDA   Irish Mist getting a clear run on the rails, followed by Uranus, King Herod sneaking up on the outside, followed by Percy Boy, followed by Champagne Charley, with Sky's The Limit and Take a Gamble well back in the field . . .

ERICA   Don't mind her. When Jedda was a baby she was trapped in a burning pram for several hours.

JEDDA   Was I?

41

ERICA   Yes, and if you don't shut up I'll put you back in there.

    (HARLEY staggers into the kitchen in his red underpants.)

HARLEY   Who's this, Erk?

ERICA   This is Alison Ashley. This is my brother Harley.

ALISON   Pleased to meet you, Harley. How's school?

HARLEY   What school?

ALISON   Missionary school.

HARLEY   This is some weird kid, Erk. I don't know what she's talking about.

    (HARLEY exits.)

ERICA   They take a vow of silence at missionary school. They're not allowed to mention it outside the monastery.

ALISON   Oh!

ERICA   And in case you're wondering, he got a special dispensation from the Pope to wear red jocks.

    (JEDDA takes two sausages.)

MUM   Jedda!

    (MUM indicates that ALISON hasn't eaten yet. JEDDA takes a sausage from her own mouth and offers it to ALISON.)

42

JEDDA   You want a sausage, Alison?

ALISON   Could I have a tissue, please?

         (There is a roar of motorcycles off as VALJOY's friends
         arrive.)

VALJOY   That's Spider and Blonk.

         (VALJOY puts down her plate and jumps to her feet.)

MUM   They're not coming in the house.

VALJOY   Oh, that's not fair, Mum!

LENNIE   What's your pick for the fifth, Jedda?

JEDDA   Guinea Gold. He always wins on a heavy track.

MUM   Last time Spider washed his leather jacket in the
         sink without asking.

LENNIE   Isn't she cute?

ERICA   She sounds like a beery old derelict at the TAB.

MUM   And you're not going out dressed like that!

VALJOY   Get lost!

         (VALJOY exits.)

MUM   (To ALISON) Do you have any pain-in-the-neck
         brothers and sisters, love?

ALISON   No, there's only me. I'm the only child.

         (LENNIE shakes up a Coke can.)

43

LENNIE   (To ALISON) Watch this. Think quick! (He squirts MUM, who squeals and giggles.) Gets her every time!

ERICA   (To ALISON) Have some sauce.

(Shouting and revving of bikes outside.)

MUM   (Yells) Will you boys get off to your own homes? If you've got any, which I doubt.

VALJOY   (Off) I'm never allowed to invite my friends home!

MUM   This place is always neck deep in creepy-looking tech kids who've been suspended from school.

(LENNIE jumps up looking at his watch.)

LENNIE   Uh-oh! Time for the big race!

(He grabs a radio and switches it on. A race caller is heard . . . .)

CALLER   Flashing light is on . . . racing in the Civic Handicap. Himalaya missed the start by a length but the rest got away in a good line. Racing quickly from an outside gate to head them off is Prince Charming, with Cro-Magnon Man settling in behind him and back behind them is Beldale Beauty . . .

JEDDA   Sweep, sweep, sweep, sweep!

MUM   It's too late for a sweep, Jedda, the race has started.

(LENNIE switches the radio off.)

44

LENNIE   No, I'll turn it off. Here, got the envelopes all made up. (LENNIE produces them.) Come on, everyone pick a horse.

(JEDDA and MUM pick slips of paper from the envelope and read the names of their horses.)

JEDDA   (Disappointed) Noddy.

MUM   (Pleased) Beldale Beauty.

JEDDA   Oh, you've got three there, Mum!

(MUM lays two slips on the table.)

MUM   Cro-Magnon Man for Harley and Devil's Disciple for Valjoy.

LENNIE   Come on, Alison, one for you too. Lucky dip.

ALISON   Oh, I . . .

LENNIE   Got to be in it to win it.

(ALISON takes a name.)

ALISON   Himalaya.

(Groans from LENNIE, MUM and JEDDA.)

LENNIE   That's a roughie, love. Never mind.

(He offers the envelope to ERICA.)

ERICA   I'm not doing it.

MUM   Oh, come on, Erk, they've started already.

45

(LENNIE picks for her.)

LENNIE Rising Fury for Erk and Prince Charming for me. And they're racing!

(He switches on the radio. ALL listen, LENNIE, MUM and JEDDA getting very excited, ALISON bewildered but enjoying it, ERICA disgusted, but becoming involved as Rising Fury looks like having a winning chance.)

CALLER As they round the home turn, four hundred to run, it's Prince Charming leading them into the straight, half a length from Beldale Beauty with Noddy and Rising Fury ranging up on the outside. Prince Charming is weakening on the turn and is gathered in by Noddy. Rising Fury challenging now . . . Noddy, Rising Fury, Noddy, Rising Fury, anybody's race, but wait, here's a dream split for Himalaya coming from nowhere under the whip. Noddy is gone, Rising Fury just holding Himalaya fifty out, but Himalaya's finishing too well and Himalaya's going to win it! Himalaya by a head from Rising Fury, Cro-Magnon Man took third place with a late run, Prince Charming fourth . . .

(LENNIE switches off the radio.)

MUM Well done, Alison!

LENNIE Boy, you can pick 'em! Have to take you to Randwick some time.

JEDDA What's the prize?

MUM We forgot to put our money in!

LENNIE Ah, just a bit of fun. Here, Alison, let's say you

46

won the last sausage. How would that be, eh?

(LENNIE offers it to ALISON.)

ALISON Oh, I've had plenty to eat thank you. I really ought to go, Mrs Yurken.

LENNIE Put it in a doggie bag for you.

(LENNIE wraps it in a tissue and hands it to ALISON.)

ALISON Oh, thank you. And thank you for having me, Mrs Yurken. I've had a very nice time.

LENNIE You're a real nice well-behaved kid, Alison.

MUM You come round any time, love. Erk doesn't get on very well with other kids as a rule.

ERICA Mum!

MUM Erk, get up off your numberplate and say tata nicely.

(ERICA leads ALISON to the door. Behind them the scene changes back to the classroom.)

ERICA Don't take any notice of them, Alison. Valjoy and Lennie and Jedda and that . . . they're not really, um . . .

ALISON It's all right, Yuk. It's just . . . it's certainly very different from Hedge End Road.

ERICA (Mimicking) 'It's certainly very different from Hedge End Road.'

ALISON Yuk, I didn't mean . . .

47

ERICA   You snob, Alison Ashley!

ALISON   I am not a snob!

ERICA   You think you're so great, Alison Ashley! You look down your nose at anyone and everyone at Barringa East. You think you're so fantastic, just because you live over on Hedge End Road.

ALISON   I've got to live somewhere, haven't I?

ERICA   How dare you criticise Barringa East! I never even invited you round here in the first place!

ALISON   What are you yelling at me for? What on earth did I do, Yuk?

ERICA   You are the most low-down person I ever met in my life, Alison Ashley! Goodbye!

(ALISON runs off, very upset. Behind ERICA the scene changes back to the classroom. BARRY, DIANE, MARGEART and ALISON enter, followed by MISS BELMONT.)

(MISS BELMONT addresses the class.)

MISS BELMONT	Listening in a moment please ... Hey! (MISS BELMONT waits for absolute silence.) When you're quite ready ... As you know, next week grade six will be going on the annual camp. This is an extremely important part of our year, the highlight of the school year, an event which is not only good fun, but which also fosters character building and team work. At the camp, you will be supervised by Mrs Wentworth from the Infants' School ... (Sniggers from THE KIDS.) ... Mr Kennard from grade five ... (Groans from THE KIDS.) ... and myself! (Dead silence.) You will each take a blue consent form home, get your parents to sign it and bring it back on Monday. At the camp you will be sharing a bunk room with other students from your grade. I would therefore like everyone to take one of these yellow forms and write down the names of two people with whom they would most like to share a room at the camp. (She passes out blue and yellow forms. EVERYONE writes. ERICA looks around the room, then puts up her hand.)
ERICA	Miss Belmont.
MISS BELMONT	Yes, Erica?

49

ERICA   Miss Belmont, could I please have a single room at this camp? It's this chronic insomnia I suffer from . . .

MISS BELMONT   Erica Yurken, you have an exaggerated sense of your own importance. There are no single rooms at this camp, so kindly write down two names and stop being so neurotic. (A bell rings. THE KIDS rush out.) You may go. Hand your forms in to me on the way out.

(Only ALISON and ERICA are left in the room, hesitating before filling in their forms. They look at each other with hostility.)

ERICA   I'm not putting your name down, Alison Ashley. No way.

ALISON   Who'd want to be in with you, Erica Yurken? It would be like sharing a room with a piranha.

ERICA   Don't you dare call me a piranha, you rotten little goldfish!

MISS BELMONT   For heaven's sake you two! Write down some names and go! (ALISON writes, slams her form down on the pile and hurries to the door. ERICA sticks out a foot to trip her, but ALISON notices it in time and coolly steps over it. ERICA sticks out her tongue at ALISON as she exits. She hesitates for a long time, starts to write, stops herself, starts again, stops, and finally writes. Then she packs up. She discovers ALISON'S consent form for the camp.) What have you got there, Erica?

ERICA   It's Alison Ashley's consent form for the camp, Miss Belmont.

50

MISS BELMONT	Alison Ashley should have taken it with her, shouldn't she?
ERICA	Yes, Miss.
MISS BELMONT	Because if Alison Ashley does not return that consent form, signed by her parent or guardian, to the school on Monday, Alison Ashley will not be permitted to go on the camp, will she?
ERICA	(Smiles to herself.) No, Miss Belmont.

(MISS BELMONT exits. The set changes back to ERICA'S house. ERICA still holds the consent form.)

(MUM enters.)

MUM   But we're going out with Lennie this afternoon!

ERICA   I have to take it round to her place, Mum.

MUM   If you ask me, Erk, you just want to stickybeak at this Alison Ashley's posh house.

ERICA   Course I don't. (Behind her the scene is changed to ALISON'S house as she continues . . .) Why should I have the slightest interest in Alison Ashley's house . . . at number 23 Hedge End Road? Where lawns look like still green pools, and every house with its pretty garden has gleaming wide windows, and the cars parked in every driveway are polished twentieth-century magic coaches. (She stops.) Why should I care if Alison Ashley's house has the most beautiful front door you've ever seen, carved wood with amber panels on each side?

(MUM exits.)

(ALISON lounges in her tastefully designed house. Sound of tinkling chimes. ALISON gets up and opens the door to discover ERICA.)

ALISON   Hello, Yuk!

ERICA   Hello, Alison. I found your consent form for the camp.

ALISON   Oh, thank heavens you brought it, Yuk! I was wondering what I was going to do. Come in.

ERICA   I can't stay. My sister's in the Olympic swimming team and I have to help coach them.

ALISON   Do you?

ERICA   I hold the stopwatch.

ALISON   Really?

ERICA   And write down their times on a clipboard.

ALISON   Oh.

(Awkward pause)

ALISON   Wouldn't you like to come in and have a drink? I can make milkshakes.

53

(ERICA hesitates, then curiosity gets the better of her.)

ERICA　All right.

(ERICA enters, looks around the house.)

ALISON　What is it?

ERICA　Your house is . . . so tidy.

ALISON　My mother's a bit fussy. I always have to clean things up straight away.

(ALISON moves through to the kitchen, forcing ERICA to call after her . . .)

ERICA　Where's your dad?

ALISON　Ssh! (ERICA is puzzled.) Mum's having a sleep upstairs.

ERICA　(Whispers) Where's your dad?

ALISON　They got divorced last year.

ERICA　(ERICA starts to ask . . .) Oh! Did your dad go off with . . . ? (Then she changes it to . . .) That's not as bad as losing your father in a tragic plane crash. You can still go and visit him, can't you?

ALISON　Not when he's gone off to Canada and hardly ever writes or anything. (Pause) I'd invite you into my room to play records but I don't want to wake up my mother. She works very long hours at the weekend.

ERICA　Which hospital does she work at?

54

ALISON   Who?

ERICA   Your mother.

ALISON   She's not a nurse. She owns a restaurant.

ERICA   Like a pizza parlour?

ALISON   No, it's a proper licensed restaurant with wait-
ers. They have silver candlesticks on the tables
and velvet chairs ...

ERICA   Oh!

(Pause)

ERICA   We could play Hats.

ALISON   What's Hats?

ERICA   It's a word game. Everyone has to think of a
different hat in turn, and if you can't think of
one by the count of ten, you're out.

ALISON   It sounds fun.

ERICA   When my father was in the Antarctic gathering
rock specimens for the museum, all the men
used to play Hats when there was a blizzard on
and they couldn't leave the tents.

ALISON   I thought your father was a test pilot.

ERICA   He was a geologist as well.

(Pause. ALISON brings milkshakes.)

ALISON   Haloes and beekeeper's nets.

55

ERICA   What?

ALISON   Bank robbers' balaclavas and Viking helmets with horns.

ERICA   We haven't started yet.

ALISON   I have. Fireman's helmet. Go on, Yuk.

ERICA   Riding cap. One . . . two . . .

ALISON   Baby's bonnet. One, two, three . . .

ERICA   Surgeon's operating cap. One . . . two . . .

ALISON   Diamond tiara. One, two, three, four, five, six . . .

ERICA   Those lace things Spanish ladies wear on their heads.

ALISON   You mean mantillas.

ERICA   (Loudly) I was just about to say mantilla!

ALISON   Ssshhh! Executioner's hood with slit eyes. One, two, three, four, five, six, seven, eight, nine . . .

          (ERICA can't think of a hat.)

ERICA   I'd better go. I've got to go down to the racetrack and get my mother's friend's horses loaded on the float.

ALISON   What about the Olympic swimming team?

ERICA   I do that every second Saturday. I just remembered today is my racetrack Saturday.

56

ALISON   Well, thanks for bringing my consent form over.
          See you on Monday, then.

ERICA   Yeah, Monday.

          (ERICA starts to go, then ALISON calls her back.)

ALISON   Go out the back way, you might wake up my
          mother . . .

          (ERICA knocks over her stool as she changes
          direction.)

ERICA   Oh, sorry.

          (A woman's voice is heard off, cross.)

VOICE   Alison?

          (ALISON freezes.)

ALISON   Yes, Mum?

VOICE   I particularly asked you, Alison. You know very
          well how demanding that job is. Clattering
          about down there. Who on earth have you got
          out there anyway?

ALISON   Oh . . . No-one.

ERICA   No-one?

VOICE   Who is it?

ALISON   I mean it's just a kid from school. Nobody really.

ERICA   Nobody! So I'm a nobody am I?

57

VOICE	Alison!
ALISON	It's all right, Mum. Yuk, I didn't mean . . .
ERICA	(Yells) Drop dead, Alison Ashley!
ALISON	I don't want you to get into trouble . . .
ERICA	See if I care, Alison Ashley! We'll see who's nobody!

(ERICA runs off, leaving ALISON distraught.)

ALISON	Yuk!
VOICE	Alison . . . Alison, come here immediately!

(ALISON slowly collects up the empty milkshake containers, carefully wipes the table clean, and exits sadly – the loneliest girl in the world. Blackout.)

END OF ACT ONE

ACT TWO

THE DORM

(MR KENNARD backs into the room, KIDS pushing and shoving in front of him. MR KENNARD yells ineffectually into a megaphone . . .)

MR KENNARD	Campers, campers, wait a minute! Listening in please . . .
DIANE	Get out, Barry!
BARRY	I was first!
ERICA	I bags a top bunk.
MR KENNARD	There's no hurry, campers.
DIANE	I bags a top bunk too.
MARGEART	Sir, I've lost my sponge bag.
MR KENNARD	We're not going in until you're quiet . . .
ERICA	Barry took it, Margeart.
BARRY	I never. I found it.
MR KENNARD	Campers, children, please!
DIANE	He pinched it.

BARRY	Twenty cents reward, otherwise I'll squeeze out all your toothpaste.

(A fight breaks out. MR KENNARD is powerless to stop it. His megaphone goes on the blink. MISS BELMONT enters. She roars . . .)

MISS BELMONT	DO YOU MIND? (THE KIDS shuffle into a line. MR KENNARD jumps into line too. Then she notices him.) I'm sorry, Mr Kennard. I didn't know there was a teacher in here.

MR KENNARD	Yes, I'm here, Miss Belmont.

(BARRY HOLLIS sneaks out as MISS BELMONT takes control.)

MISS BELMONT	I would remind you that while we are at this camp we are relying on each other and ourselves. We are ambassadors for Barringa East and I expect you to behave as such. Mrs Wentworth, Mr Kennard and myself are giving up a week away from our families, without paid overtime, I may add, and anyone stepping out of line will be sent home in disgrace. (BARRY HOLLIS passes the window behind MISS BELMONT.) Barry Hollis, I can see you! Put that fire extinguisher back where you found it immediately! (BARRY ducks for cover, amazed at the eyes in the back of MISS BELMONT'S head.) When you have unpacked your things, leave your huts tidy and come quickly and quietly to the dining hut for roll call. You have five minutes.

(MISS BELMONT and MR KENNARD move to the door. MR KENNARD looking sheepish.)

MR KENNARD	Thank you, Helen. I don't know how you do it.

(MISS BELMONT looks at MR KENNARD with disdain, taking the megaphone and ejecting the dead batteries as they exit. ERICA, ALISON, DIANE and MARGEART rush into the dorm and take possession of their bunks.)

MARGEART   This one's mine.

(ERICA bounces on a couple of beds, then returns to the bunk she chose first, only to find that DIANE has already taken it.)

DIANE   I bags this one.

ERICA   Get off, Diane. I need that one.

DIANE   Why?

ERICA   I have to have a firm solid mattress because of my fused vertebra.

ALISON   You haven't got a fused vertebra, Yuk.

ERICA   That's all you know, Alison Ashley. When I was eight I fell off a bolting horse.

DIANE   Bull.

ERICA   I was rounding up cattle on my uncle's cattle station in the Northern Territory. They had to get an army helicopter to rescue me.

DIANE   Well, I'm the group leader of Kangas and I'm keeping this bunk, so tough.

(With bad grace, ERICA unpacks her tatty sleeping bag on the less desirable bunk. Meanwhile ALISON makes up her bed with sheets and a quilt.)

63

MARGEART   My nan has a bad back. It's called lumbago. I
           never knew kids our age could catch lumbago.

DIANE   Hey, look at Yuk's old sleeping bag!

ERICA   It may look old and battered but it's very
           valuable. It was used on the first expedition to
           climb Mount Everest.

DIANE   It just looks old to me.

ERICA   Well, look at this then.

           (She starts to unpack a stack of VALJOY's slinky
           clothes from her suitcase.)

MARGEART   Oh wow, look at Yuk's clothes!

DIANE   Oh, give us a look, Yuk!

MARGEART   Are you allowed to wear high heels, Yuk?

ALISON   How come you never wear any of these clothes
           to school?

ERICA   I save them for the Cascade Disco on Saturday
           nights.

           (MARGEART reads a label on the back of a pair of
           jeans.)

MARGEART   Who's 'Valjoy'?

           (ERICA grabs the jeans back again.)

ERICA   That's the name of the designer. She's very
           famous in Italy, but of course you wouldn't
           know that.

64

MARGEART   Ohhhh!

(DIANE finds VALJOY's black nightie.)

DIANE   Ohhhh!

MARGEART   Ohhhhh!

DIANE   Ohhhh! Yuk, can I wear this one morning at breakfast?

(ALISON takes no part in the admiration ritual. She unpacks her own clothes, including a beautiful oriental dressing gown. MISS BELMONT enters.)

MISS
BELMONT   Why, Alison, what a lovely dressing gown! You're a very lucky girl to own such a beautiful thing!

(ALL HEADS turn to look at it.)

ALL   Ohhhh!

ALISON   My mother bought it overseas somewhere. But it's not very useful really.

DIANE   Give us a look, Alison.

MARGEART   Can I see?

DIANE   Can I try it on?

(ERICA knows she is upstaged.)

ERICA   We can't all have mothers who nip overseas and buy us dressing gowns just to take on a school camp.

65

(ERICA throws herself down on her bed.)

MISS BELMONT
And Erica, I don't want you lounging around on that bed all week.

(MISS BELMONT spots VALJOY's clothes.)

MISS BELMONT
And whatever are all these?

ERICA
My clothes.

MISS BELMONT
They're not your clothes. I can tell by the size. (MISS BELMONT starts to load them into a plastic bag.) You can collect all this at the end of the camp. I can see I'll have to keep a very close eye on your behaviour during the week. Honestly, Erica, haven't you ever been away from home before?

(Pause)

ERICA
(Realising that she hasn't) No.

MISS BELMONT
You're in grade six now. It's high time you learned how to take care of yourself.

(She exits, taking the clothes with her. ERICA is about to burst into tears, and hides her face in the pillow. BARRY HOLLIS sticks his head through the doorway. Then he sees ERICA and comes and inspects her closely.)

BARRY
Yuk's bawling.

ERICA
I'm not.

BARRY
Yes, you are, there's a big wet patch on the pillow.

ERICA   I'm allergic to foam rubber if you must know.

(ALISON crosses to ERICA, concerned.)

ALISON   Are you all right, Yuk? (ERICA buries her head in the
         pillow.) Want me to get one of the teachers? (OTHER
         KIDS come round to watch. ALISON sits beside ERICA.) Are
         you homesick?

(ALISON lays a hand on ERICA'S shoulder, but ERICA
throws it off.)

ERICA   Leave me alone, Alison Ashley. I certainly didn't
         put your name down on my form. There's no
         way I would have chosen to share a room with
         you for a whole week!

ALISON   I didn't put your name down on mine, either.
         You needn't think I did. Who'd want to share a
         room with a cactus?

(ERICA runs from the room.)

(MR KENNARD enters, carrying the megaphone. After a couple of attempts he manages to get it to work.)

MR
KENNARD

Listening in, please, campers. There are just ten minutes left to lights out, so after you have cleaned your teeth and put on your pyjamas, I want all huts to settle down . . .

(MISS BELMONT beckons to MR KENNARD out of the shadows. She carries a torch and a cardboard carton.)

MISS
BELMONT

Coming to eat, Mr Kennard?

MR
KENNARD

But we've just had dinner.

MISS
BELMONT

Frankfurters, frozen peas and instant mashed potato is not my idea of food, Andrew. Can I borrow your Swiss Army knife? (He finds it for her.) Well done.

MR
KENNARD

I thought I'd better come prepared. (MR KENNARD watches uneasily as MISS BELMONT uses the knife to slice up quiche and camembert and open a bottle of wine. In the meantime he continues his announcement . . .) Remember that it is strictly against camp rules to eat food in the dormitory huts. And anyone caught eating junk food of any description will be severely punished.

68

(Then MR KENNARD weakens and joins MISS BELMONT with the food. They exit together.)

(THE GIRLS sit around a candle, eating a midnight feast. They are playing 'Hats'. ERICA is playing too, but sits apart from the other three.)

ALISON Bobby's helmet.

DIANE School hat.

(It is ERICA's turn.)

ALL One, two . . .

ERICA Cricket cap.

(MARGEART thinks hard.)

ALL One, two, three, four, five, six . . .

MARGEART Hair.

(Groans from DIANE and ERICA.)

DIANE You can't say 'hair', Margeart.

ALISON Margeart, it has to be a sort of hat. Something you wear on your head.

ERICA She's out.

70

ALISON	No, give her another go. Coronet.
DIANE	Sunhat.
ERICA	Mortar board.
ALL	One, two, three, four, five, six . . .
MARGEART	Hair curlers.

(Groans. There is a tapping at the window and a pasty hand starts to write 'BEWARE' backwards.)

DIANE	What's that?

(There is a spooky groan from outside.)

MARGEART	(Terrified) It's . . . it's writing Chinese! (The hand suddenly remembers to use mirror writing in order that those inside should get the 'BEWARE' message. It rubs it out and starts again.) It's a ghost!
ERICA	(Warily) It's not.
ALISON	It's Barry Hollis.
BARRY	I'm coming to get you-ooooose!
ALISON	What are you doing, Barry?

(BARRY climbs in through the window, covered in a sheet and white powder.)

BARRY	Better lock the windows tonight, girls.
DIANE	What for?
BARRY	So the Basin Skins don't get youse.

71

ERICA   That's rubbish!

MARGEART Who are the Basin Skins?

BARRY   They're a real tough lot. Tougher even than the
          Eastside Boys in Barringa East. First night of the
          camp, every year, that's when the Basin Skins
          come up the mountain and give this place a real
          going over.

ERICA   Rubbish.

BARRY   They sneak in when everyone's asleep. About
          midnight, that's when they strike.

ERICA   Rubbish. Last year's grade six always spread
          that story of the Basin Skins, just to scare the
          next lot coming up here. They don't even exist.

BARRY   Last year they tattooed my brother's head
          without even waking him up.

ALISON   No-one could do that.

BARRY   This place is haunted too. Something real pecu-
          liar comes out of the creek and claws the
          windows.

DIANE   Oh yeah?

BARRY   That's how our school can afford it here. We're
          their only customers. No other school in the
          State's game enough to come here.

ERICA   Rubbish!

BARRY   And this happens to be the room where the
          murder happened. Under that bed you can see

72

the bloodstains.

(ALISON leans across to look, brushing BARRY's hand. He screams. Everyone else screams too, then tries to look cool. MARGEART whimpers.)

ALISON   It's all right, Margeart. There's no bloodstains there.

BARRY   Bet you all start bawling tonight and want to go home.

DIANE   Don't be ridiculous.

MISS   (Calls) Lights out, everybody. (EVERYONE freezes. She
BELMONT   enters.) NOW! (They all dive into bed. BARRY conceals himself under a sheet and attempts to sneak around behind MISS BELMONT, but the eyes in the back of her head track him down.) Don't you have a hut of your own to go to, Barry Hollis?

(The sheepish figure under the sheet shuffles out of the room. MISS BELMONT exits. Silence. THE GIRLS sleep. ERICA climbs out of bed, checks under the bunk for bloodstains, and looks out the window for a sight of the Basin Skins. She starts at sounds in the night. Wrapped in her sleeping bag and carrying her torch, ERICA exits.)

(Outside the hut there is a public telephone booth. ERICA enters, picks up the telephone and dials. MUM's voice is heard.)

MUM   Hello?

ERICA Hello, Mum . . . it's Erica.

MUM   Erica! What's the matter? Have you broken your leg or something?

ERICA No.

MUM   Or is it snakebite? Or is the camp surrounded by bushfires?

ERICA I only wanted to chat.

MUM   Erk, it's 1.30 in the morning. I thought it might be that weirdo who rings people up and says he's poisoned their cat. And it turns out to be only you! Go back to bed, now!

(She hangs up. ERICA turns to see BARRY HOLLIS watching her. He is as scared as she is, spooked by his own tales of the Basin Skins and bloodstains. Nevertheless he grins slyly.)

BARRY Who are you ringing? Your Mum?

74

ERICA	Certainly not! As if I'd be doing anything so immature! (Into phone) I'll give you another ring tomorrow night, Leo, after all the little kids are asleep. And on Saturday I'll be free to go parachute jumping with you. Bye . . . darling.

(ERICA hangs up.)

BARRY	Who's Leo?

ERICA	Someone I know.

(BARRY knows who it really was.)

BARRY	Finished with the phone? Got to ring my girlfriend. (BARRY dials.) I often ring her at funny hours. She doesn't mind. Get away. This is very private!

(ERICA eavesdrops. BARRY'S MUM'S voice is heard.)

MRS HOLLIS	Hello?

BARRY	(Attempted sexy) Hello, it's Barry.

MRS HOLLIS	Why are you ringing at this ungodly hour, Barry? And why didn't you take your parka with you after I sewed the name-tag on specially? And if you're not behaving yourself I'll belt you one when you get home!

(MRS HOLLIS hangs up.)

ERICA	Was that your Mum, Barry?

BARRY	Well, what about you? Some guy called Leo!

ERICA	Why did you ring her? Were you scared, Barry?

75

BARRY   Scared of what?

ERICA   Scared of the Basin Skins.

BARRY   I'm not scared of anybody.

(MISS BELMONT enters.)

MISS
BELMONT   Oh, aren't you indeed?

(THE KIDS run off. MR KENNARD enters, carrying a guitar.
He strums it behind MISS BELMONT, unintentionally
giving her a big fright.)

MR
KENNARD   How about this? We could do a Hawaiian act,
with hula dancing . . .

MISS
BELMONT   What are you talking about, Andrew?

MR
KENNARD   For Drama Night – the teachers' item.

MISS
BELMONT   Andrew, if you think you're getting me poncing
about in a grass skirt you've got another think
coming.

MR
KENNARD   But the teachers have to do something.

MISS
BELMONT   We'll be flat out finding seats for the parents and
sorting out the chaos backstage. The kids can
take care of the acts. Let them entertain us for a
change. It will do them good. (They exit, MR KENNARD
strumming.) And I don't want to hear that thing
again till you've learned more than three
chords!

(It is the next morning. ERICA studies her play-script
as ALISON, DIANE and MARGEART run out, playing 'Hats'.)

ALISON   French beret.

DIANE   Party hat.

ALL   One, two, three . . .

(ERICA doesn't realise it is her turn, then looks up just
in time.)

ERICA   Sombrero.

(ERICA returns to studying her script, subvocalising
the words of 'Pirate Peg', trying to memorise the
lines, while acting out a swordfight scene.)

ALL   One, two, three, four, five, six . . .

MARGEART   Bald head.

(Groans. BARRY HOLLIS wanders out, playing with a
Swiss Army knife very much like Mr Kennard's.)

ALISON   Crash helmet.

DIANE   Straw hat.

77

(Pirate Peg doesn't realise that everyone is waiting for her.)

ERICA   So hoist the Jolly Roger,
And load the cannons grim,
For Captain Blood approaches . . .

ALL   One, two, three, four, five, six, seven, eight, nine, TEN!

DIANE   You're out, Yuk!

ERICA   That's not fair. I wasn't watching.

DIANE   That's not our fault.

ERICA   I have to learn my lines, don't I?

ALISON   But you've been learning them for weeks, Yuk.

ERICA   That just shows how little you know about theatre, Alison Ashley! All great actresses come to the very first rehearsal with all their lines learned so they don't even have to bring the script.

DIANE   It's only a play for Drama Night, Yuk.

ERICA   If that's your attitude, Diane, it's just as well that someone in Kangas is taking the trouble to do it properly. You may not mind getting up in front of all the parents on Drama Night and making a fool of yourself, but I'm playing Pirate Peg and I intend to do it very well.

(MISS BELMONT enters and claps her hands for attention.)

MISS BELMONT	Listening in, Kangas. In activity time this morning I want you to think up an original idea for a play for Drama Night. At previous camps, people just sat back and let the teachers do all the work . . .
ERICA	Aren't we doing *Pirate Peg of the Jolly Roger*?
MISS BELMONT	Not this year, Erica.
ERICA	But they always do *Pirate Peg*! They've been doing it for years!
MISS BELMONT	Exactly. Dragging that tired old pantomime out of the cupboard again is not my idea of creative drama at all.
ERICA	Couldn't we just use bits of *Pirate Peg*? We could jumble up the lines . . .
MISS BELMONT	Certainly not. I want a brand new play from each group. The play can be about anything at all, but I certainly don't want to see any violence or anything in poor taste that will give Barringa East a bad name. So jump to it - now!

(MISS BELMONT exits. ERICA throws herself on to the ground and howls her frustration.)

DIANE	Anyone got any good ideas for plays?

(No-one has. There are a number of half-hearted suggestions, attracting no support from any other Kangas . . .)

MARGEART	What about *Robin Hood and his Merry Men*?
BARRY	*The Boston Strangler.*

79

DIANE   We could put on a mannequin parade or a
          beauty contest.

BARRY   *Jack the Ripper*. Bags me being Jack.

DIANE   She said no violence. Jeez you kids, come on,
          will you? Ideas! (To ALISON) Can you think of
          something?

ALISON   I'm trying to, but I just can't.

MARGEART I thought the group leader of the Kangas was
          supposed to think up the ideas.

DIANE   The group leader's just the organiser. Everyone
          has to help with ideas.

ALISON   Why don't you ask Yuk? (All eyes turn to ERICA. She
          panics, then recovers.)

ERICA   As a matter of fact, I have a very good idea for a
          play.

DIANE   What?

ERICA   It could be set in a hospital. With an operating
          theatre scene and we could get some sausages
          and kidneys and liver to make it realistic.

DIANE   Hey yeah, with doctors and nurses.

BARRY   And blood!

ERICA   And a visitor coming in drunk from a football
          match.

BARRY   Parramatta!

80

ERICA   Naturally the matron will be the main part, and naturally I'll act that, seeing I'm the one that thought up the idea.

DIANE   What about costumes?

ERICA   Well, Alison Ashley's got enough white clothes to outfit a hospital, and everyone's got pyjamas. Shove some chairs together to look like a row of hospital beds. (They do this with great enthusiasm, while ERICA scribbles notes.) Margeart, you get into a bed and be a patient, 'cause they don't have to say much. Diane can be the nurse. And then I come on as the matron making a tour of inspection. She's a very bossy matron. Everyone has to shake with terror when she runs her fingers along looking for dust. This is the way the matron should be acted. (ERICA prepares to make a big entrance. Then she dries up.) Um . . . I think it might be better if the matron came in from this door here.

DIANE   What for?

ERICA   Look, I'm making up this play and I know how it has to be done. The matron comes in like this.

        (ERICA makes another big entrance, then freezes with stage fright when all eyes are on her.)

BARRY   Pretty funny matron, just opening and shutting her mouth.

        (ERICA fumbles for her notes.)

ERICA   Um . . . I've come to . . . I'm here to make a . . . ward inspection. Nurse Jackson . . .

81

(ERICA falters to a stop, her voice a mere squeak.)

MARGEART   Isn't the matron supposed to be bossy?

(ERICA looks at her notes, braces herself and tries
again.)

ERICA   I'm here to make a ward inspection. Nurse
Jackson, um ... (BARRY giggles. ERICA covers up.)
What we really need is a director. We'll leave
out the part of the matron for the moment and
go on to the drunk visitor arriving. That's Barry
Hollis.

BARRY   Who says I'm acting in any dumb play?

ERICA   I do. No-one else is foul-mothed and grotty
enough to do the part except you.

BARRY   (Complimented) You reckon?

(He takes up his position.)

ERICA   Now, this is what you do. You come in and
you're drunk see, so you fall down on the
ground. And then the matron comes in ... (She
realises that this is her again) I can't be expected to
write this play and direct it and do every little
job single-handed. I need a temporary stand-in
to be the matron till I've got the whole thing
worked out.

DIANE   Alison, then.

ALISON   I couldn't act a big part like the matron. I'd feel
embarrassed.

(ERICA takes this in – her big chance to see ALISON

82

ASHLEY embarrassed.)

ERICA   There's no need to be embarrassed. This is what
         the matron has to say . . . (She reads from her notes.
         It is not a great reading, but much more confident
         than when she was in the spotlight . . .) 'I'm here to
         make a ward inspection. Nurse Jackson, what is
         this patient doing on the floor? How dare you
         leave patients lying around untidily like that
         during visiting hours! Kindly put him back into
         bed this minute.' Only of course you have to put
         in a lot of expression and actions and every-
         thing. Go ahead, Alison, there's absolutely
         nothing to it!

ALISON   I've never acted before. Couldn't I just be a
         patient like Margeart?

ERICA   It doesn't matter how stupid you sound reading
         out this part now, because I'll be taking over and
         doing it on Drama Night.

ALISON   All right then.(ALISON moves awkwardly to her posi-
         tion and clumsily mimes opening the door. ERICA is
         enjoying ALISON's discomfort. Then suddenly ALISON
         launches into it – a great impersonation of MISS BELMONT's
         manner.) I'm here to make a ward inspection.
         Nurse Jackson, what is this patient doing on the
         floor? How dare you leave patients lying around
         untidily like that during visiting hours! Kindly
         put him back into bed this minute! (The OTHER KIDS
         are very impressed, but ALISON is still hesitant.) Did I
         say it right?

ERICA   Not bad.

DIANE   What do you mean, 'not bad'? She was fantastic!

83

ERICA   She's only the understudy!

ALISON Yes, sure, Yuk.

ERICA   I have to finish writing it this afternoon. We'll rehearse again tomorrow morning.

(THE KIDS exit.)

(ERICA goes to the phone and dials. HER MOTHER'S voice is heard . . .)

MUM   Hello? Yurken Mansions.

ERICA   Mum? I have to rush. I'm on my way to rehearsal. I've got the main part in the play.

MUM   Really, love?

ERICA   I'm the hospital matron.

MUM   Oh, that's wonderful, Erk! I can hardly wait to come up and see you on Friday night. Just fancy, playing the lead role!

ERICA   Well, there's no-one else here who can act.

MUM   Wonderful! Now, about the matron's costume. Lennie's got a mate whose daughter's a vet's receptionist. I'm sure she's got a white dress. Oh, I just feel so proud!

ERICA   It's nothing, Mum. See you Friday.

(She hangs up. MISS BELMONT enters.)

MISS BELMONT   Erica Yurken, you're late for sport. Get into line at once.

85

ERICA   Miss Belmont, can I be excused from sport? I
           come out in eczema if I touch a netball.

MISS   Go!
BELMONT

           (MISS BELMONT exits. ERICA runs off and meets BARRY
           HOLLIS.)

BARRY   You going to sport?

ERICA   Of course not. I'm much too busy writing the
           play.

BARRY   You ought to write a play about me.

ERICA   Why?

BARRY   My whole life would make a great play. Once I
           lived in a charity clothes-bin for a week.

ERICA   Sure. Your life would make a great play. For
           people training to be convicts.

BARRY   I didn't have a shower for ten days.

ERICA   So?

BARRY   I thought you'd be grateful, getting my idea. I'll
           only charge you a dollar for it.

ERICA   Get lost.

BARRY   Interest fifty cents if you don't pay up on
           Wednesday. Worth a lot to a writer, a good idea.

ERICA   I'm not usually a writer. I'm only doing this as a
           favour since everyone else is so stupid. I'm
           really going to be an actress.

86

BARRY   But you're hopeless.

ERICA   Hopeless?

BARRY   You'll never be an actress. We all saw you. As
             soon as you had to act with people looking at
             you, you got so scared you couldn't say a word.
             Like I said, you're hopeless at acting.

                   (BARRY exits. ERICA suffers. ALISON enters, carrying a
                   white apron.)

ERICA   What are you staring at, Alison Ashley?

ALISON   I've made the matron's apron for you, Yuk.

ERICA   Better try it on and see if it fits you.

ALISON   What for?

ERICA   I . . . I won't have time to act in the play on
             Drama Night. I'll be too busy.

                   (ERICA stalks off.)

ALISON   Oh! All right, Yuk.

                   (Very excited about getting the role, ALISON runs
                   to the phone and dials. ALISON'S MOTHER'S voice is
                   heard . . .)

MOTHER   Hello? Jennifer Ashley.

ALISON   Hello, Mummy, I didn't mean to disturb you,
             but it's about the Drama Night.

MOTHER   Oh, I'm sorry, Alison, I'm going to have to work
             on Friday.

87

ALISON   But Mummy, you promised you'd come!

(ERICA sneaks back towards the phone to
eavesdrop.)

MOTHER   I know Alison, but it's going to be such a busy
night at the restaurant.

ALISON   You needn't stay for supper afterwards, just for
the play.

MOTHER   Alison . . .

ALISON   It's only short. All the other parents are coming.

MOTHER   All the other parents don't have busy restau-
rants to run.

ALISON   Can't you get someone to fill in for you?

MOTHER   Alison, this is all totally unreasonable. You know
I have a very important job and I simply don't
have time to rush off to a little school concert.

ALISON   Oh, that's what you always say! Please!

MOTHER   Alison!

ALISON   Sorry, Mummy.

MOTHER   Goodbye, darling.

(ALISON hangs up. ALISON leaves the phone, close to
tears. ERICA comes up to her.)

ERICA   Alison . . . (Perhaps she is about to comment on
ALISON'S surprising show of emotion, but at the last
minute she changes it to . . .) Can you lend me

88

thirty cents? I have to make an emergency phone call and a magpie just swooped down and stole my purse.

(But ALISON just runs off. MARGEART enters, rehearsing lines.)

MARGEART I am very sick, Nurse Jackson. I am very sick, Nurse Jackson.

(ERICA picks up two burnt sticks from the ground.)

ERICA Hey, Margeart?

MARGEART Hello, Yuk.

ERICA You want to see what I just found?

MARGEART What?

ERICA You promise not to tell anyone?

MARGEART Why?

ERICA Just promise.

MARGEART All right. (ERICA shows her the sticks.) Gosh! (Then puzzled) What are they?

ERICA They're genuine Aboriginal firesticks. See the burnt ends?

MARGEART Gosh! Where did you find them, Yuk?

ERICA Um, quite close to the barbeque area.

MARGEART Gosh! Can I see them?

ERICA	No, you might break them.
MARGEART	I won't.

(Pause)

ERICA	I'll sell them to you if you like.
MARGEART	How much?
ERICA	Thirty cents.

(MARGEART takes out the money. The sticks are exchanged.)

MARGEART	Gosh!

(MARGEART exits. ERICA goes to the phone and dials. MUM'S voice is heard . . .)

MUM	Welcome to the madhouse!
ERICA	Hello, Mum?
MUM	Erk, love, I'm glad you rang. I've been thinking about that matron's costume . . .
ERICA	Mum . . .
MUM	I can make a hat out of serviettes . . .
ERICA	Mum . . .
MUM	. . . from the Pizza Hut.
ERICA	MUM!
MUM	Don't shout, dear.

ERICA   What I phoned to tell you was, I just heard the road to the camp's been blocked by a landslide and the bulldozers won't get it clear till after Drama Night.

MUM   Nonsense, Erk. You don't think we'd let a little thing like a landslide stop us coming to see you act in a play.

ERICA   But Miss Belmont doesn't want the camp littered up with parents on Drama Night.

MUM   Oh, Erk! They like the parents to take an interest.

ERICA   Some kids' parents aren't coming. I don't think Alison Ashley's mother will.

MUM   That's terrible!

ERICA   She has to work or something.

MUM   Well, we'll be there hail, rain or shine, don't you worry. Lennie even got his shift changed specially.

ERICA   Did he?

MUM   You bet he did. He wouldn't miss out on your concert for anything.

ERICA   Mum, I might not be in the play. I've got this really bad sore throat.

MUM   I've got to go, Erk. Our cat's just bailed up next door's German Shepherd. See you tomorrow night, love.

(She hangs up. ERICA yells into the phone . . .)

ERICA   But I don't want you to come!

(She hangs up. MISS BELMONT enters. She finds the script of the play which ERICA has dropped on the ground in front of her.)

MISS
BELMONT   What is this bundle of scrap paper?

ERICA   It's the script for the Kangas' new play, Miss Belmont.

MISS
BELMONT   Then kindly pick it up, Erica, and put it where it belongs.

(MISS BELMONT exits. ERICA picks up the script, looks at it for a moment and throws it into a rubbish bin. She exits.)

(In the dressing room, THE KIDS are getting ready to go on stage. Much yelling and excitement as they try on their costumes.)

DIANE   Shut up, you kids! Can't you even keep quiet for twenty minutes? Practise your lines or something. It's only twenty rotten little minutes to Drama Night.

(MARGEART, clutching a pillow, suddenly bursts into tears.)

MARGEART   Awwwwww!

DIANE   What's the matter with you?

ALISON   What is it, Margeart?

MARGEART   I don't want to wear that!

DIANE   But you have to. You have to be the pregnant lady with the pillow up your dress!

MARGEART   I don't want a pillow up my dress!

ALISON   You have to have a pillow, Margeart, otherwise you won't look pregnant.

MARGEART   I don't want to look pregnant! I don't want to be in the play at all.

93

(MARGEART climbs under a bed.)

BARRY   Hey, where's all the meat for the operation scene?

(ERICA enters.)

DIANE   Yuk's the stage manager. She said she was getting it.

ERICA   Oh, I . . .

DIANE   You didn't forget, Yuk?

BARRY   We'll have to leave that bit out.

DIANE   We can't – that was the best part!

BARRY   And where's the beer bottle I was going to have? How can I be a drunk without a bottle?

DIANE   And where's my nurse's hat?

BARRY   And tomato sauce for blood!

DIANE   And where's Alison's matron's hat? And the balloons for the nurse's big bosoms? You call yourself a stage manager!

(ERICA panics but puts up a brave front.)

ERICA   I don't know why you're all panicking. All the props for this Drama Night have naturally been taken care of. I was just about to go out and collect them.

(ERICA exits.)

(ERICA sits, head buried in her hands. LENNIE approaches her.)

LENNIE   How yer going, movie star?

(ERICA affects nonchalance.)

ERICA   Oh, hello Lennie.

LENNIE   It's been a quiet old week without you. Your mum's gone ahead to grab some seats down the front, but she sent me over to give you this. (He opens a box and pulls out a matron's cap.) She sat up half the night making it. Hope it fits you all right, otherwise I might have to come up and play the matron myself. (He tries on the hat.) What do you reckon? (ERICA bursts into tears.) Hey, steady on, Erk. What's the matter?

ERICA   Everything! You know how I told Mum I was going to be the star of Drama Night? Well, I'm not.

LENNIE   Of course you will be!

ERICA   I won't. I'm so hopeless at acting I'm not even going in the play. I'm too scared.

(LENNIE doesn't really know how to handle this.)

95

LENNIE   Well, don't worry. Not everyone can be a great actor. I'd be petrified.

ERICA   And when I wrote the play it seemed pretty good . . .

LENNIE   You wrote the play?

ERICA   Yes, but it's so dumb and nobody wants to be in it and the audience will all get up and leave in the first five minutes.

LENNIE   No, they won't.

ERICA   And I said I'd be the stage manager, but I was so busy being the director that I forgot all the props we need, so there's no sausages for the operation scene and no balloons for the nurse's bosoms . . .

(ERICA collapses, sobbing on LENNIE's shoulder. He hugs her hard, pleased to finally be accepted and needed by her.)

LENNIE   Hey, don't cry, Erk. She'll be apples, love. A few missing props is nothing to worry about. Let's see what's fallen off the back of my truck.

(LENNIE takes ERICA by the hand and leads her off.)

(MARGEART is still under the bed.)

DIANE   Come on out, Margeart. We can't do the play without you.

MARGEART   No.

DIANE   Please, Margeart. We need you to be the pregnant mother.

MARGEART   No!

BARRY   I'll be the pregnant mother.

(BARRY demonstrates.)

DIANE   No!

(ERICA enters, her red eyes hidden behind LENNIE's driving glasses. She starts to dole out props from a cardboard box.)

ERICA   Here we are. Sausages for the operation, a hat for the matron, a bottle for Barry the drunk and boobs for the nurse. I told you it was all taken care of.

BARRY   What about Margeart?

97

(MARGEART is still clutching the leg of the bed.)

ERICA   Come on out, Margeart. We've got all the props now, so there's nothing to worry about.

MARGEART   I'm not doing it.

DIANE   You'll have to be the pregnant mother, Yuk.

ERICA   Me?

DIANE   There's nobody else. Get the costume off Margeart.

ERICA   I can't do it.

DIANE   You'll have to, Yuk. You know all the lines and everything.

ERICA   I . . .

DIANE   Get a move on.

ERICA   I . . . can't.

DIANE   Why not?

ERICA   Because I . . . I . . .

(The OTHER KIDS stare. Then ALISON rescues her. She grabs MARGEART and screams at her . . .)

ALISON   You come out of there, Margeart! Erica can't possibly get dressed in time and have her face made up. A lot of work went into fixing this play. If you go mucking up Drama Night you'll look like a lump of strawberry jam once I've finished with you! I'm going to count to three, and if you

98

don't come out by then I'll tear out your liver and use it for the operation scene.

(Shocked at this display from ALISON, MARGEART crawls out from under the bed and meekly puts the pillow up her dress.)

DIANE   Good, now get on stage. We're starting.

(DIANE, BARRY and MARGEART exit. ERICA removes her dark glasses.

ERICA   Thanks, Alison.

ALISON   That's all right, Yuk. Lots of people are too scared to be actors. But not very many can write great plays. Oh, I nearly forgot, I've got a present for you.

(ALISON hands ERICA a present. ERICA unwraps a bound folder and reads the cover . . .)

ERICA   *'Barringa East Hospital* – a play by Erica Yurken.' Oh, Alison, it's great.

ALISON   That's OK. I couldn't stand seeing that script end up in the bin.

ERICA   'By Erica Yurken.' I'll have to change my name if I'm ever going to be a famous writer.

ALISON   I saw your mum and her security guard in the front row. Are you going to sit with them?

ERICA   No, I'll be too nervous. I'll sit up the back.

ALISON   All right.

(ERICA and ALISON start to go, then turn back to look at each other.)

ERICA   Good luck, Alison Ashley.

ALISON   Thanks.

(ALISON exits. ERICA looks proudly at her book, then puts on her dark glasses and exits too.)

(ALISON walks on stage in front of the house curtain.)

ALISON   Ladies and gentlemen, the Kangas present *Barringa East Hospital*, a play written especially for Drama Night by Erica Yurken. Scene One – in Barringa East Hospital.

(She exits through the curtain. It jerks open to reveal the hospital ward. MARGEART, a patient, lies in one bed, with a second (empty) bed beside her. At the foot of each bed is a medical card. DIANE, wearing enormous balloon boobs, enters as NURSE JACKSON. The acting is very stilted.)

DIANE   Good afternoon, Mrs Higginbotham. How are you feeling today?

MARGEART   I am very sick, Nurse Jackson.

(DIANE points to the medical card at the foot of the bed.)

DIANE   I see from your hospital card that you are suffering from ... (Big breath) hiatus hernia arthritis diabetes and bee-sting allergy.

MARGEART   Yes, and what is more, I think my baby is going to be born at any minute.

101

DIANE   Your baby is going to be born at any minute? Let me see. (MARGEART gets out of bed and with some embarrassment shows a huge pregnant stomach.) I do believe you are right, Mrs Higginbotham. I must call matron immediately. And can I ring your husband too?

MARGEART   Yes. He is at the football match, watching Parramatta.

DIANE   Then I shall ring him at the ground. We can not have him missing the baby being born.

MARGEART   By the way, Nurse Jackson, where is that nice Mr Belmont who was in that bed yesterday?

DIANE   I'm afraid that nice Mr Belmont died last night.

MARGEART   Oh, how sad.

DIANE   Yes, but he was suffering so much it was really a merciful release. (She takes the medical card from the foot of his bed.) He had suspected hypersensitivity to (Big breath) wattle pollen horsehair dust mite clover and Clag glue. And he was covered all over in eczema from a lifetime of touching netballs.

MARGEART   How sad. Well, good-bye, Nurse Jackson.

DIANE   Good-bye Mrs Higginbotham.

(DIANE exits. The curtain is drawn. ALISON steps through the curtain.)

ALISON   Scene Two. In Barringa East Hospital, half an hour later.

102

(She exits. The curtain opens again. The scene is unchanged, with MARGEART still in bed. BARRY enters as an outrageous drunk, holding a bottle and wearing a Parramatta scarf.)

BARRY Parra-matta! Up the mighty Eels! C'mon, Sterling, tackle him! Bring him down, that's the stuff.

(He tackles a bed.)

MARGEART Get up, darling, the baby is just about to be born.

BARRY Baby? What baby?

MARGEART Our baby.

BARRY You mean to say you brought me all the way from the football just to watch a baby being born?

MARGEART It *is* an emergency!

BARRY They told me it was an emergency!

(MARGEART has given her line too early, but now repeats it.)

MARGEART It *is* an emergency.

BARRY And what about Parra? The match of the day is just about to start.

(ALISON, as the matron, enters with DIANE the nurse. ALISON roars, Belmont-style . . .)

ALISON Do you mind! I'm here to make my ward

inspection. Nurse Jackson, what is this patient doing on the floor? How dare you leave patients lying around untidily like that during visiting hours! Kindly put him back into bed this minute!

DIANE   But matron, he's not a patient.

ALISON   I'm going to count to one, Nurse Jackson, and if he's not in bed by then there's going to be a hole in that window your size and shape in the next three seconds!

DIANE   Very good, matron. (To BARRY) Upsadaisy!

          (She puts him into bed.)

BARRY   Hello, sweetheart, you're a good-looker! Reckon I'll come to hospital more often.

DIANE   Get your hands off me, you brute!

          (In the ensuing tussle one of DIANE's boobs bursts.)

BARRY   Sorry, cutie.

          (DIANE panics. This was not in the script. She grabs a grapefruit from beside MARGEART's bed and stuffs it down her dress.)

MARGEART Hey, Diane, I'm supposed to eat that!

          (A moment of confusion, then ALISON saves the situation.)

ALISON   I'm sorry, Mrs Higginbotham. Patients are not allowed to eat before serious operations.

BARRY   You wouldn't happen to know the football

104

score, would you, love?

ALISON   Certainly not. Now, Nurse Jackson, hold this patient down while I give him an injection.

BARRY   But I'm not a patient! I'm a visitor!

ALISON   Absolute nonsense! I've been matron of this hospital for twenty years and I should think I know a patient when I see one. You are very, very sick.

BARRY   But I feel fine.

(ALISON inspects the medical card.)

ALISON   Mr Belmont . . .

BARRY   My name is Mr Higginbotham.

ALISON   Mr Belmont! You may feel fine, but you are suffering from an advanced case of hypersensitivity to wattle pollen, horsehair, dust mite, clover and Clag glue. And you have the worst case of netball-induced eczema I have ever seen. I'm afraid we'll have to operate immediately.

BARRY   Operate?

DIANE   Operate, matron? But that is the doctor's job.

ALISON   This is a matter of life and death, Nurse Jackson.

BARRY   (To DIANE) What time do you get off work, cutie?

ALISON   I think he needs an injection with our biggest needle.

105

DIANE   It will be a pleasure, Matron. (DIANE takes a huge
         syringe.) Be brave, Mr Belmont! This won't hurt
         – much!

BARRY   No, no, you can't do this to me!

         (They grapple for the needle. It bursts DIANE'S
         remaining inflatable.)

DIANE   Now look what you've done!

         (DIANE grabs MARGEART'S second grapefruit.)

MARGEART Diane!

         (But DIANE is getting the idea of ad libbing.)

DIANE   This is an emergency, Mrs Higginbotham.

         (ALISON creeps up behind BARRY and hits him on the
         head with a mallet.)

ALISON   Got you! You horrible little man!

BARRY   Ohhhh!

         (BARRY collapses on the bed in a spectacular faint.)

ALISON   Now, Nurse Jackson, put the screen around the
         bed and we can start the operation.

MARGEART What about my baby?

ALISON   Mrs Higginbotham, we can't do every little job
         at once. Your baby will just have to wait.

MARGEART But ...

106

ALISON   We're very busy people. Just take a pill and try
           not to worry. (Some hesitation, then the curtain is
           drawn. ALISON steps through it.) *Barringa East Hospi-
           tal*, Scene Three. In the operating theatre.
           (Screams from BARRY backstage. ALISON steps back
           through the curtain as it opens. MARGEART'S bed has
           gone. A screen has been set up around BARRY'S bed
           and the operation can take place as a shadow show
           on a sheet.) Nurse Jackson?

DIANE   Yes, matron?

ALISON   Hand me the big knife. I'm going to cut him
           open.

               (BARRY sits up.)

BARRY   Cut me open?

ALISON   Nurse Jackson, give the patient some more
           anaesthetic.

               (DIANE, struggling with the grapefruit, hits BARRY on
               the head with the mallet.)

BARRY   Ohhhh!

               (BARRY falls unconscious again.)

ALISON   Nurse Jackson, the knife. (DIANE hands over a
           butcher's knife. In shadow show, ALISON cuts BARRY open.)
           Oh, deary, deary me, Nurse Jackson. No wonder
           this patient is so sick! We got to him just in time.
           (She pulls out a succession of revolting objects. Then
           she pulls out a heart.) Uh-oh! Better put that back
           again. (She replaces it.) And he hasn't been
           chewing his food properly!

               107

(She pulls out a lot of unmasticated food, finishing with a string of sausages and a bottle of beer. MARGEART enters.)

MARGEART   Matron ...

ALISON   Mrs Higginbotham, get back into bed immediately!

MARGEART   I am going to have a baby.

ALISON   I haven't got time for that yet, Mrs Higginbotham. I'm doing a very important operation.

(She gestures to MARGEART to get back into bed. Her appearance is apparently too early.)

MARGEART   I am going to have a baby. Now.

ALISON   Sew him up, Nurse Jackson. The operation is over.

(MARGEART delivers a doll from under her costume.)

MARGEART   I've had my baby – look! It's a boy!

(She displays it, but the pillow is also still in place and has to be disposed of by DIANE. BARRY staggers to his feet, shirt open, covered in blood.)

BARRY   Let me see.

ALISON   Wait, Mr Belmont, we haven't sewn you up yet!

BARRY   But I want to see my baby. (He takes it.) How're yer going, footy star? (He wraps his Parramatta scarf around the infant's neck.) Ready for the game?

DIANE   Mr Belmont, bring that baby back!

ALISON   Mr Belmont!

MARGEART I feel quite faint!

(A chase follows as MARGEART, ALISON and DIANE pursue BARRY around the room.)

BARRY   Come on, son, if we hurry we'll catch the second half. Carn the Eels!

(BARRY exits with the baby. They chase him off. Curtain. The cast come out and bow.)

ALISON   Author!

(ERICA comes through the audience, climbs on stage and takes a bashful bow. DIANE'S grapefruit make a final bid for freedom. DIANE makes an official speech.)

DIANE   On behalf of grade six I'd like to thank the parents for coming to see our Drama Night, and I'd like to thank the kitchen staff for cooking all the delicious meals and I'd like to thank the teachers for giving up their valuable time.

(DIANE leads applause, then all exit through the curtain.)

(THE KIDS know the performance has gone really well. Much mutual backslapping and general celebrations. MISS BELMONT enters.)

MISS BELMONT   Excellent work, everyone. Very good indeed. Barry, Diane, that was excellent. You too, Margeart. Alison, you were marvellous! (ERICA stands to one side, modestly allowing the cast to get their plaudits. BARRY and MARGEART exit. Then MISS BELMONT notices ERICA.) Erica, it's one of the best grade six plays I've seen on a Drama Night. Well done!

ERICA   Thank you, Miss Belmont.

DIANE   Hey, did you see your parents laughing, Yuk? You could hear your dad through the whole hall!

ERICA   Oh, he's not really my . . .

DIANE   He was great! When he started laughing it got everyone else going.

(DIANE exits.)

ERICA   Yeah, Lennie's really enthusiastic.

(MISS BELMONT notices something happening in the flytower).

110

MISS BELMONT Barry Hollis, get down from there this minute! (BARRY HOLLIS (Off) gives a Tarzan yell.) And let Margaret go!

(MARGEART, bound and screaming, is swung in on a rope and lowered to the stage. MISS BELMONT unties her.)

MISS BELMONT There's always one silly person who spoils it for everyone else.

(She exits. MARGEART looks out through the curtain.)

MARGEART Which one is your mother, Alison?

ALISON Oh, my mother ... um ... she isn't ... I mean, she couldn't ...

(ALISON turns away, fighting back tears. ERICA steps in to save her.)

ERICA Mrs Ashley isn't here tonight. She's an air-traffic-control technician and airports can't close down just because there's a concert on.

MARGEART Gosh!

(MARGEART exits. ERICA goes to comfort ALISON.)

ERICA Listen, your mum might have started to drive up here and found a big tree fallen across the road. (No answer from ALISON.) She might have started to drive up here and found an injured Saint Bernard dog and turned back to take it to the animal hospital. (No answer.) she might have had a very good reason. Maybe she couldn't phone and tell you because there was a gale-force wind and all the power lines were down in Hedge End Road.

111

ALISON   It isn't because of that at all. She didn't turn up for the same reason she never does. She's not interested in anything I do. She won't even be there at school tomorrow to meet the bus.

(Pause)

ERICA   How are you getting your case home?

ALISON   The same way I got it to school when we left for camp. It's only a five-minute walk.

ERICA   We could give you a lift in Lennie's truck.

ALISON   Thanks, Yuk. That'd be great. (ALISON grins.) Lennie's got time off tomorrow, has he, from being a security guard at your mansion over by Kyle Grammar?

ERICA   All right, smarty. He's not a security guard. He's a truckie.

ALISON   No, he's not. You can do better than that. He's a circus acrobat who broke his collarbone and your mum's nursing him back to health seeing she used to be a bareback rider in that same circus and that's how they met.

(MUM and LENNIE enter.)

MUM   Erica, you're sly! Letting me think you were acting in the play like all the other kids and all the time you were the writer! It was so funny! I never knew you could write!

ERICA   It's just a knack.

LENNIE   We've got some news for you too.

112

ERICA   What?

MUM   Lennie and me are getting married.

LENNIE   We're going to announce it at a surprise party
tomorrow night. But we wanted to tell you first.

ERICA   Oh, Mum!

(ERICA hugs and kisses MUM and LENNIE.)

MUM   Alice, do you want to come to the party?

ERICA   Her name's 'Alison'. Gee, Mum, I wish you'd
get my friends' names right!

LENNIE   You'd be most welcome, love.

ERICA   And you can stay the night if your mum'll let
you. Say 'yes', please say 'yes'.

ALISON   Thank you, Mrs Yurken. I'd like that very much.

LENNIE   Good.

(LENNIE and MUM move aside to rummage around in
the props.)

ERICA   'Mrs Yurken.' Gee it sounds horrible!

ALISON   But if your mum marries Lennie, you could
change your surname to Lennie's name.

ERICA   Hey, yes, it would be nice to have something
more sophisticated than 'Yurken'.

ALISON   What is Lennie's surname?

113

ERICA   I don't know. We always just call him 'Lennie'.
Hey, Mum, what's Lennie's surname?

MUM   Grubb.

ERICA   What?

ALISON   (Laughs) Oh, Yuk! That would be really sophisticated. You could change your name to . . . 'Erica
Grubb'!

(ERICA is furious, then she laughs too.)

ERICA   I hate you, Alison Ashley!

(Both dissolve into helpless laughter as the lights
fade.)

END OF ACT TWO

About Robin Klein

Robin Klein is the much-loved and acclaimed author of more than forty children's books. Many of these have been shortlisted for the Australian Children's Book of the Year Award, including *People Might Hear You* (1984), *Hating Alison Ashley* (1985), *Halfway Across the Galaxy and Turn Left* (1986), *Seeing Things* (1994) and *The Listmaker* (1998), which also won the 1998 South Australian Festival Award for Literature.

Her outstanding novel, *Came Back to Show You I Could Fly*, won a Human Rights Award for Literature in 1989 and the 1990 Australian Children's Book of the Year Award for Older Readers. It was also shortlisted for the 1990 Victorian Premier's Literary Award and the 1990 NSW Premier's Literary Award, and named a White Raven book at the 1990 Bologna Children's Book Fair.

In 1991 Robin Klein was awarded the Dromkeen Medal for her significant contribution to the appreciation and development of children's literature in Australia.

About Richard Tulloch

Richard Tulloch has written over thirty plays which have been performed in all states of Australia as well as overseas. They include *Year 9 Are Animals*, *If Only We Had a Cat* and adaptations of Gillian Rubinstein's *Space Demons* and Randolph Stow's *Midnite*.

He is also the author of over twenty children's books, including *Stories from Our House*, *Stories from Our Street* (both illustrated by Julie Vivas), and KOALA Award nominees *Danny in the Toybox*, *The Brown Felt Hat*, *Being Bad for the Babysitter* and *Barry the Burglar's Last Job*.

Richard has five times been nominated for Australian Writers' Guild AWGIE awards, and in 1988 won AWGIES for *Talking to Grandma while the World Goes By* and *Hating Alison Ashley – The Play*. In 1993 he formed his own theatre company, Joined-up Writing, to produce *Unbeatable!*, based on stories by Paul Jennings, and his own play *Danny in Trouble*.

At the last count he had written ninety-four episodes of the children's television hit series *Bananas in Pyjamas*.

Father's Day

Anne Brooksbank

What if your parents had been keeping a secret from you your whole life?

Sam is in his first year of high school and has been saving his paper-round money for months to buy the one thing he yearns for – a boat. Suddenly his bank balance is doubled by an unknown person. But who is it? As Sam investigates he watches in dismay as his family life is turned upside down; and he is forced to make a decision that will change everything.

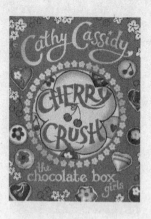

Cherry Crush
Cathy Cassidy

Cherry Costello's life is about to change forever. She and Dad are moving to Somerset where a new mum and a bunch of brand-new sisters await.

And on Cherry's first day there she meets Shay Fletcher; with suntanned skin and sea-green eyes he's the kind of boy who should carry a government health warning.

But Shay already has a girlfriend, Cherry's new stepsister, Honey. Cherry knows her friendship with Shay is dangerous – it could destroy everything. But that doesn't mean she's going to stay away from him...

Thai-No-Mite!

Oliver Phommavanh

I'm Lengy and I'm Thai. My parents run a restaurant named Thai-riffic! but I'm always craving hot chips and pizza.

Mum and Dad's idea of a holiday?
Going to Thailand to visit all our relatives.

Recipe for getting there?
- Survive Dr Needlemouse and his arsenal of needles
- Squeeze in a snappy budget trip to Dreamworld
- Catch a red-back spider for my Auntie
- Fight off a savage bat attack
- Celebrate Christmas, Thai-riffic style!

Recipe for surviving the planning?
A heap of good luck and plenty of THAI-NO-MITE! Phew! I'll need a holiday after this…

The Accidental Princess

Jen Storer

Inside the lilac hedge, two sets of glittering emerald eyes observed Matilda through the heart-shaped leaves. 'It is the princess!' whispered a tiny voice . . .

When the pixies and fairies of the lilac hedge mistake Matilda for royalty, she is drawn into a wondrous world. But evil forces threaten the hedge and its folk, and Matilda must fight to save her new friends. She can't do it alone, but could it mean losing her sister forever?

Fans of *The Magic Faraway Tree* and the *Narnia* series won't be able to resist *The Accidental Princess*!

The Candymakers
Wendy Mass

In the town of Spring Haven, four children have been selected to compete in the national candymaking contest of a lifetime. Who will make a candy more delicious than the Oozing Crunchorama or the Neon Yellow Lightning Chew?

The contestants face off in a battle of wits and sugar, but soon they realise that things are not what they seem, and they find themselves in a candy-filled world of surprises, suspense, and mouthwatering creations.

In this charming and cleverly crafted story, award-winning author Wendy Mass cooks up a delectable concoction of mystery, friendship, and juicy revelations.

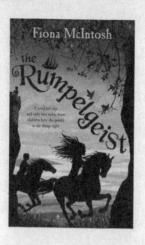

The Rumpelgeist

Fiona McIntosh

Drestonia's capital is cursed by hauntings and disappearing children, panicking the city. Curiously it seems only Crown Princess Ellin, with the help of a young noble, Flynn Jolien, has the power to solve the dilemma. The problem is Flynn's been seriously injured by a rival for Ellin's attention and his only chance of survival depends on the magic of the contrary and elusive sorcerer, Grendel.

Ellin must use all her courage and wit as she embarks on a dangerous journey against enemies known and unknown to find Grendel, save Lord Jolien's life and return the stolen children of Floris to their parents.